THE PHOEBE'S NEST

An Illustrated Collection
of Poems and Stories

by James S. Benedict, M.D.

JB-97

Illustrations by the Author

JB Press - 1998

Other Books by **JB PRESS**

Poems of a Civil War Veteran
Matthew Cowlin - 1991

Big I and little i
James S. Benedict, M.D. - 1992

Eva - An Autobiography
Eva Besaw-Button-Fuller - 1993

Exhibition from a Poem Museum
James S. Benedict, M.D. - 1993

Poems from the Concert Hall
James S. Benedict, M.D. - 1994

The Empty Shell
James S. Benedict, M.D. - 1996

Library of Congress
Catalog Card Number: 98-91344

ISBN 1-892015-00-5 (Hard Cover)
ISBN 1-892015-01-3 (Soft Cover)

ADAMS PRESS
CHICAGO, IL

FOREWORD

Many of our friends and family are aware that in 1978, we purchased property on a small lake in Northern Michigan. We have been traveling back to our cabin there each summer. My previous poetry books have had many poems inspired by our stay there. Other prose stories have been a natural outcome of our experiences in the woods. It is a wonderful place to meet our families, our friends and our natural visitors. When casting about for a title, a theme, if you please, for this latest collection of poems and stories, *Benedict's Bower* seemed a good choice. Therefore, this particular volume has been organized around birds, animals and nature. I have tried not to repeat poems that were published in earlier books, and have not included any of the many bird Christmas cards that I send out each year.

In the summer of 1997, Muriel and I went to France for our first visit to that interesting and exciting country. There is a section on French poems, most of them written while there. The illustrations for these poems were also mostly made as sketches while touring the country. A few were added from slides and brochures after returning home. In the summer of 1996, I spent a week at the Iowa Writers' Conference, several poem pieces were a result of that experience. Later in the same summer, I spent another week at *The Frost Place,* seven days of idea exchanges with other poets at Robert Frost's former home in New Hampshire. Several poems resulted from this workshop and it will be apparent upon reading the book, which they are.

i

The professors in the English Department at Cal State University Long Beach have also been particularly helpful the past two years. I would like to thank Elliott Fried, Charles Webb, Robert Spiese, David Peck, and Roxanne Sexauer for their guidance and help with this material. Very few of these poems have been submitted for publication as I have not had the time to send them off. By putting them all together in this volume, I feel they will be properly presented with appropriate illustrations. Hopefully they will be appreciated by friends or family who have read my work before.

If all goes according to plan, I will graduate with my Bachelor of Fine Arts in December of 1998. What the future holds after that is not certain, perhaps work towards a Master's Degree. I hope my work at the University has resulted in this volume being better than the previous ones. With Kinko's Copiers readily available as a "second office", it has made the labor of putting this book together easier than previously. With the semester break here, I hope to complete this work and get it to the printers shortly.

My wife, Muriel, has been very supportive of my efforts to put this collection of poems and illustrations together. I thank her for it. Other members of the family have been encouraging me to continue to write. The stories are strictly fiction, though based on actual places and events. If names, places, and events seem to be true, it is strictly coincidental and not intended. There may be mistakes, please excuse them.

Finally, I want to thank you, my readers, for your continued support of my writing efforts.

Jim Benedict - January 1998

THE PHOEBE'S NEST

An Illustrated Collection
of Poems and Short Stories

TABLE OF CONTENTS

POEMS FROM THE NORTH WOODS
AND OTHER PLACES

POEMS FROM THE TOUR DE FRANCE

POEMS FROM NEW HAMPSHIRE
AND OTHER PLACES

POEMS FROM AN INNER PLACE

TALES FROM AROUND THE FIREPLACE

POEMS FROM THE NORTH WOODS
AND OTHER PLACES

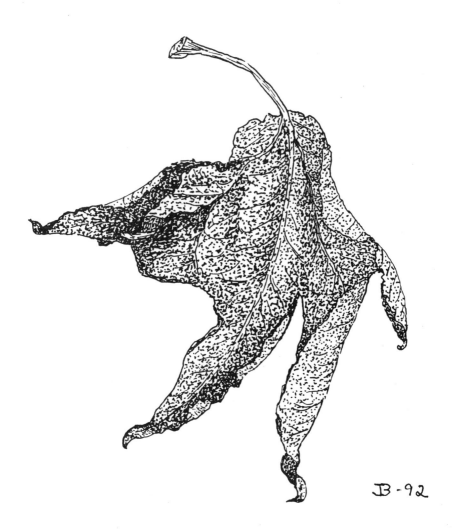

MICHIGAN BOWER

Mid-state red pine plantation
in Wilderness Valley on C-38
where Deer Lake kisses the Manistee.
Giant white pines, towering oaks,
hover over quaking aspens,
poplars and red maples,
freckled with white birches.
Cross country ski trails,
deer paths, lanes of two dirt tracks
where snowplows give up in winter.
       Beaver dams, quiet ponds,
       jumping frogs, dragon flies,
       garter snakes and snapping turtles.
       Nervous phoebes, eagle skies,
       hungry house finches, chickadees,
       woodpeckers and hummingbirds.
       Grasshoppers, wasps and honey bees,
       gypsy moths, deer flies,
       flying bats and carpenter ants.
       Fall colored tapestry
       Christmas card snow,
       Jack-in-the-pulpit,
       thunderstorms and rainbows.
Porcupine up a tree,
skunks beneath the shed,
loons floating and fishing on the lake.
Trilliums pushing up through April snow,
blackberries feeding bears,
hordes of mosquitoes in the air.
Fallen spruce trees, rotted logs,
firewood piled out back,
frosty autumn, northern lights.
Long days of summer
whip-o-will singing nights,
racoons robbing bird feeder,
moths circling the light.
Old wooden dock, floating canoe,
biting fish, fire flies too,
red sunsets, golden clouds,
morning mist and moist dew.

Rough log honeymoon cabin,
up in the north woods,
screened in front porch,
sweet smell of cooking pies.
Social hall, family reunion,
visitors, lost strangers,
neighbors, friends, the forest ranger.
Clear starry nights,
moonrise over the water,
red embers in the fireplace,
bone weary sleep.

Poems and stories come from this cabin.

WALNUT TREE

Walnut tree so tall,
towered majestically over all.
Strong, straight it grew,
nuts a blackish hue.
Scores of winter frosts
had chilled its bark.
Spring rains wet, soaked
its roots, bursting buds.
Summer ripened its fruit,
squirrels hid fall nuts.
Hikers rested and marveled,
birds nested its branches.

Inside the walnut lay
a growing changing seed.
Chromosomes split, cells divided,
new ones made, multiplied.
With Nature some complied,
others rebelled, lost control,
defied rules, but why?
Normal processes gone awry?

Saplings sprout and grow
from buried kernels now.
Some are deformed, bent,
others shrivel, die away.
Storms rage, water's dammed,
channels close, Nature fails.
Capsules burst, bones bust,
tree limbs wither, break.
Sap no longer runs
termites chew the grain.
Leaves are blown away,
tree is bare today.
Then old tree falls,
plunges to mother earth,
where it rots, decays,
and soon passes away.

Nature again is done,
walnut tree has gone.
The forest is silent,
only its nuts remains.

PHOEBE NEST

Beneath our bedroom window awning,
I see four tiny bird beaks spread wide open.
A nest of grass, mud holds their yawning,
carefully designed by some master plan.
In this miniature phoebe house,
parents stuff insects and flying things
into those bottomless gaping mouths
on fuzzy balls without feathers or wings.

I stand and gaze over nest's rounded edge
at the buff breasted mother with brownish head.
The father's a nervous twit on the porch's ledge,
his dark crowned brain just wants me dead.
Both parents flutter, fly, to and fro,
from apple tree twig to branch to nest.
They bob their tails like cello bows,
wishing their babies could get some rest.

Cold May nights slip into warm June days,
spring buds burst into leaves upon the trees.
Those adult phoebes catch bugs in so many ways,
while babies grow feathers above their knees.
The nest seems smaller, not even room for three,
so the young fall out and began to fly.
They coast from home to a white birch tree,
wobbling and gliding across the summer sky.

The nest is now vacant, the little ones gone,
woven threads, sticks and mud, an empty pall.
I do not hear any quiet chirping song,
the dark forest has engulfed them all.
Another set of offspring has fled this year,
nervous parents flit around our window sill.
Oh, how soon, little ones grow up and disappear.
That phoebe nest is bare, how silent, how still.

AUTUMN SONNET

The apples are red in the orchard,
pears are ripe on their trees.
Cornstalks are dry and turning brown,
their drooping ears hang full of corn.
Fields of wheat and oats ripple yellow,
while woods become a rainbow of color.
The harvest moon glows orange
and frosty nights turn dew white.
Grandparents jostle newborn babies
and families gather around a turkey.
Leaves fall, barren trees stand alone,
and loved ones leave us lonely, forlorn.
But God is in the great blue heavens,
and prepares a place for coming winter.

FLICKERS

I hauled sand all morning
from the sand pit down the drive
to fill the holes in the path
that leads down to the lake.
Packing, raking, then seeding down,
flat as an airplane runway,
the job was finished before noon.

The afternoon sun dried the wet sand,
grass seeds sprinkled liberally,
were mixed with the fresh soil
before the ants began their invasion.
Evening came and so did the flickers,
scratching, pecking, rolling about,
poking after ants, taking a dust bath.

One large aggressive male with red head,
drove off small birds from his bath,
cavorting, flopping his wings in the sand.
Tiny grains settled among spotted feathers,
on his white rump and in his flowing tail.
My carefully planted lawn and grass
was torn up, scratched, transformed
into a barren patch of tannish sand.

But what does a morning's labor mean,
when nature gives those flickers a frolic
in my fresh sand? Long after my toil
and labor have been forgotten,
those flickers will still roll,
chase ants and have their fun.

A/P   Yellow Shafted Flickers   James S Benedict '96

9

10

THE WHITE PINE

My favorite tree
   (and the Michigan state tree),
      is the Eastern White Pine.
It stands tall and majestic
   in the northern woods
      with its massive trunk
         black with age.
Its limbs step out
   like ladder rungs,
      reaching soaring heights
with tufts of silver green
   needles, fine and delicate,
      in groups of five.
Pines grew as virgin timber
   in the primordial forest,
      as aged monarchs ruling
         over maples, oaks and poplars.
Old trees drop seeds from cones
   among unfurling ferns,
      where small trees spring up
         and compete for sunlight
in the open forest spaces.

Deer wander down their trails,
   browsing on tender branches,
      rubbing itching backs
         upon its rough bark.
Unable to put my arms
   around the massive trunks,
      I stoop and grasp
         tenderly the shoots
of new growth saplings.
The large living giants
   were here long before
      I was born,
and they will still stand
   just as awesome and handsome,
      after I am dead and gone.
So spare the white pine trees,
   find other ways to make lumber,
      to harvest logs and poles.
Let those that follow
   also love and admire
      these beautiful plants
         growing big and tall,
forever untamed and wild.

TREE

A
tree
is always
worthy of a poem.
Though there are thousands
of poems already written about
trees, here is one that lets a tree
form and shape it. As there are many
various types of poems about trees,
also there
are many different shapes of trees,
trunks and stumps in the forest.
This   format   is
used   to   give
meaning and
shape
to
this
poem
about
trees
found
in
the
woods
in
our
place
up
north.

CLEMATIS

Crawling, scrambling up the neighbor's fence,
white feathers fan from purple hairs.
Open loops of tender petals spring
from strings of royal tipped pearls.
Leaves are pointed, curved green discs,
draped from wandering reddish vines.
Bees and flies buzz among those threads,
purest white flowers gleam among the green.
Soft petals radiate from an inner core,
spreading light to my shadowed floor.

Clematis
Portland OR 6-7-90

13

CABIN BOOKSHELVES

When the Dawn Comes over Wilderness Valley,
it is seven a.m. in the middle of August
at *Uncle Tom's Cabin*. In a few months,
The Winter of Our Discontent will be here,
with the sun coming up late and leaving early.
Crossing to Sunlight will help shorten the day,
and ease the burden of *Roughing It*.
The bookcases are filled with tomes,
How to Collect Anything Book as a guide.
The cold dark nights, short days,
are when *Washington Irving's Sketch Book*
is pulled from the shelf
and *The Robe* from the closet.
The fireplace is ready *To Build a Fire*,
and it's hard to believe that
All Things are Wise and Wonderful.
The cold, melancholy rain
makes the outdoors like *Alaska*
and even brave *Ben Hur*
would not step outdoors
in such a deep winter.
Even *The Portrait of a Lady*
hanging above the stone fireplace
seems drab and dreary in winter.
In the cases among the *Treasures,*
we find in this *House of Seven Gables*
both ancient antiques
and rows and rows of books.
But now it is August, *Fair Weather*
is forecast for reading or pleasure.
Bookshelves are dusted and ready
for *The Return of the Native*,
for *The Further Adventures
of Sherlock Holmes*
or other fantastic adventures.
Whether we are there
in *The Summer of Forty Two*
or the winter of ninety six
the bookshelves are loaded
and waiting at *The Cabin in the Woods*.

BLACKBERRY PIE

Ready to eat, washed by a gentle rain,
blackberries hang in clusters
from last years violet stems.
Some are crushed, trampled by bears
romping through the patch
or where deer browsed the dark plump fruit.
Whitetails come from the cedar swamp
where young fawns were dropped in spring
and now walk carefully at mother's side.
The rough tongues that combed the fawn,
now taste the sweet berries
before bobbing its white tail over the fence.

A large doe lies dead beside the road,
turning into a few scattered white bones
mixed with roadside weeds and light tan fur.
A buck trots across the gravel highway,
stops to stare at my passing car,
turns, bounds and quickly disappears.

At a white roadhouse with its green trim,
three fat bucks, antlers poking
above their trucker's caps,
finger their morning coffee cups.
They bolt for the blackberry patch
and their favorite fresh baked pie.

WHITE PINE

White pine boughs with their needles green,
make the noblest tree in the northern wood.
Its brown seed cones are often seen
with fresh snow resting upon their hoods.
Chickadees flit, rest upon its branches,
squirrels scamper beneath its haunches.

Its black bark grows and heals
for three hundred years or so.
Three score years and ten, I feel,
have rapidly passed, I watch them go.
Only a fraction of the pine's long years
have been granted me, it appears.

With roots planted deep in the ground,
the pine stands against storms' sharp blades.
Little time remains for me, I've found,
as I stroll each summer beneath its shade.
Not many years are left to know
this majestic pine all bathed in snow.

MADE IN THE U.S.A.

Hard soapstone is black,
from West Virginia quarries.
Chisels from Gary,
Indiana cut the stone;
I sculpt a figure from rock.

Some Flint, Michigan
sandpaper smooths the surface.
An art gallery
in Los Angeles sells it,
a New York woman owns it.

LEAKING ROOF

When the rain pours down in buckets,
we find that our roof leaks and duck it.
When the rain stops and skies are fair,
we forget the crack or hole that's up there.
We can not understand why it leaks, because
trouble seems to come like a big buzz saw.
Our lives can be like wet caked table salt,
we don't know that problems may be our fault.
So we don't patch the roof when the sun shines,
and when it's raining is not the time.
So we scurry and scramble with our pails
to catch the leaky roof drops, it never fails.

JB-97

THE NEW SHED

I dug a deep trench
around a square plot out back.
I built concrete forms,
pumped mud in the foundation
from a cement truck in front.

I nail a wooden frame,
fasten it to the slab with bolts.
A door space is left,
one cut out for the window,
joists and beams slope for the roof.

I cover the sides
with wire mesh, colored stucco.
Tar paper, shingles,
then laid long in straight roof rows,
make it rain and waterproof.

My jackhammer digs
a narrow moat round the house.
Electric wires
and phone lines are buried there
to carry power, small talk.

Next, I make cupboards,
paint the walls, lights are installed.
I hang the door straight,
final touches are applied
to my brand new storage shed.

RED FOX

Last night your mind and body ran free
through northern woods and trails.
Yesterday, you chased grouse, young turkeys
with your floating, rusty, flying tail.
Your pointed nose and beady eyes
told of a spirit at complete liberty.
Sly and sneaky, yet to your own kits so wise,
you carried mouse morsels home tenderly.
Nature coated you in a coat of reddish tan,
over sand trails and deer paths where you ran.

This morning you are stretched out dead,
lying beside the asphalt road.
Your blood stains the gravel shoulder red,
your body bloated like a stricken toad.
That last sprint across the pavement
was cut short by some speeding car.
Your body is now mangled beyond bereavement,
another victim of the road kill wars.
Where ever you've gone, where ever you may be,
I hope your soul is still running free.

RACOONS

It is still dark,
a cold winter morning.
Yellow street lights flood
the Lincoln Avenue bridge
over the deserted interstate.
From a distance
they look like rats,
upon closer view,
just like cats.
The two black forms
then separate.
A smaller one scampers
to the far side,
the larger one approaches
with a rapid lumbering gait.
It's not a cat at all,
now I see, my friend,
it is a large racoon.

Its black ringed tail
floats out behind,
its masked face
suggests a committed crime.
Swiftly is passes by
as if pursued.
It jumps upon the concrete
rail, crosses the sidewalk,
and leaps into an old oak tree.
Two coons, conversation
interrupted, now both speed
in opposite directions.

Often in our own social
intercourse, we may be disturbed,
disrupted, so we also flee.
Unlike racoons, however friendly
each to each appears to be,
man can speak, think, contemplate.
We can express our fears,
tell our hopes, shed our tears.
We can give our love
to all our human peers.

21

BACK PORCH IN WINTER

Our wrought iron chairs are empty now,
summer left them behind upon the porch.
The patio table is all covered with snow,
to have a picnic, we'd need a hot blow torch.
The backyard trees stand naked and bare,
yet a few brown leaves still flutter and cling
to slender winter twigs drawing black lines there.
On weathered deck floor, a deep drift sings,
whispers, sleeps like a hibernating bear.
A frisky squirrel scampers on the sly,
across the top of the old board fence.
It blends with the gray of the worn wood sky,
scatters clumps of cotton on the pine bough hence.
Long evergreen needles are deep and dark,
against the sullen gray atmosphere.
Silence, stillness, quietude, hark!
Winter has blanketed everything here.
A few falling snowflakes float on down,
drift like dove feathers in the arctic night.
They land softly upon the frozen ground,
another layer of gloom for this frigid site.
Where are summer's barbeque smells,
the warm July sun to bake my frozen back?
When will the snow melt upon the hill,
buds burst from their dead branch plaques?
Alas, those cold iron chairs are vacant there,
a frosty white cloth still covers the table ware.

SAVE OUR COUNTRY

Move everyone into the city
and save our country.
This will stop some Oregon guy
from complaining about a rancher's
cows urinating into his river.
The misquito population will fall
as developers fill in the marshes
and birds won't dump on cars
that park near the wetlands.
Trees can grow or burn naturally,
without being cut for firewood.
Canyons can be used for landfills
without disturbing neighborhood
housing and rental associations.
West Virginia ex-farmers
can toughen their lungs in coal mines
instead of sitting on porches
smoking tobacco grown in Virginia.
Coyotes can roam the hills
without being shot or poisoned.
Cowboys can get jobs in Hollywood
or with the Marlboro Company.

If everyone goes to the cities,
grafitti will be confined to walls
and billboards will be empty.
Bears will stop mauling people,
cougars will not eat little kids.
Cow feed lot stench will not offend,
highways will be empty of cars.
Mountain climbers won't fall off cliffs,
skiers won't perish in avalanches,
and children won't drown in lakes.
Deer hunters can just shoot each other,
rural robberies will cease.
But best of all, naive poets
will only fill their minds
with rugged, realistic,
four letter trash words.
Let everyone move into the city
and save our country.

ROAD KILL

Not the bugs and gnats that are everywhere,
leaving their guts and brains on your windshield,
nor the golden wings of a soft unlucky moth,
impinged upon your front hood grill,
nor the delicate glassy wings of a dragon fly
mounted on the air intake screen,
reveal the exact scene of your murder.

But flattened frogs, belly up on rural roads,
identify the swampy marshes of northern Indiana.
Small green snakes pressed into paper curls
on New Hampshire's hills tell where they were killed.
An orange salamander is stretched out straight
on Vermont's trackless asphalt county road.
Eyeless black masks of Iowa ratoons
lie foiled on their get-a-way, stealing corn.
Northern Michigan roads are littered
with deer carcasses and porcupines useless quills.
In Wisconsin, a possum faked its death
for an on rushing menace that made it real.
Ohio highways are too wide an expanse
for darting chipmunks or running squirrels.
Moose signs mean nothing in Canada
where these large beasts are hit by trucks.
In Los Angeles, a baby dies from passing gang fire,
freeway drivers perish in drive by shootings.

Road kills tell you where you are.

A
mother

duck   swims

across   mirror-like

lake.   Tiny

ducklings
cluster,
paddle
in her
wake.

WALKING POEMS

1.

The old dog walked slowly with a measured pace,
her leash held loosely, her tan coat a shabby fur.
The hairs had turned white around her sad face,
the leash coaxed, but did not contain her.

2.

A young raccoon with black tail ringed,
scooted up an oak tree with dark eyes in relief.
It looked guilty of some crime or sin,
or was it me that was Nature's thief?

3.

Two squirrels leap-frogged across the grass,
a startled jackrabbit froze and stared at me.
Shaking and sitting still, it waited for me to pass,
I walked on by and like the squirrels, let it be.

B-90
Canterbury Bells

WIDOW'S WINTER

The lake is frozen solid, ice alone is on top.
My heart is cold, my mind is windswept free.
The trees have no leaves, twigs are bare,
my home is empty, vacant, spare.
Snow covers the dead brown grass,
my loneliness knows no bounds.
January's chill has chased the birds away,
I shiver without my mate's warm body.
Autumn's dry leaves all have fallen,
my own tears have ceased to flow.
The long dark night seems endless,
will my profound grief never cease?
I must bear the blowing blizzards,
when blowing drifts are piled high.
I feel the loss of love and lover,
will I ever again see the sky?
I long for gray sullen skies of winter
to give way someday to spring.

I listen for the robin's song
and hear my sorrow sing.
I look for the first crocus flower
while treading upon withered leaves.
I wander down the silent forest trail
to search among its barren trees.
I know the cold of this winter
has splintered my broken heart.

WINTER CABIN

It's late, midnight at their lakeside cabin,
where in the fireplace, hot coals glow red.
An exploding log is crackin', poppin',
its smokey smell wafts across their sofa bed.
The only light in the dark rustic room
gleams from an occasional flare of flame.
A bear skin rug hibernates in its tomb;
she warms curled up toes in its black mane.
The fading fire melts his inward stare;
she cuddles within his ax-muscled limbs.
He reaches out to touch her meager hair,
gently strokes her ashen face grown thin.
Even as dark dying coals help them hide,
the cancerous wind howls and cries outside.

Their mountain cabin lies quite desolate
beneath pitch-black forest of lonely pines.
The winter wind whines and whistles wet
across the wooden logs and mud caulked lines.
Smoke dwindles up the blackened chimney flue
those two persons still remain, man and wife.
Their summer neighbors (which were quite a few),
have left, gone down to the lower city life.
The glowing fire has faded from aged groins,
and glistening crystals of frozen breath
soon cloud over their frosted window panes.
Their ancient brains wrinkle, dry as death,
and ash gray hair transforms to snowy white.
A silver moon now alone rules the night.

WINTER HAIKU

Winter trees are stripped,
fences are piled high with snow.
It's cold in Denver.

Snow drifts melt slowly,
icicles hang from the eaves.
Christmas came, is gone.

Crescent moon shines bright,
A cold wind blows from the east.
No one is awake.

Books are on the shelves,
no one has time to read them.
Much hidden knowledge.

The couch is empty,
television is still off.
Football game later.

The roads are icy,
cars drive carefully. I walk
slowly on the road.

Winter walk is cold,
summer stroll is best of all.
Spring brings new pathways.

Music lulls the mind,
reading fills an empty head.
It is cold outside.

Pie makes big belly,
cake, cookies fill out my form.
Diets for the rest.

Empty nest, no birds,
snow covers the frozen ground.
It is still winter.

POEMS FROM THE TOUR DE FRANCE

SUNRISE OVER THE RIVER SEINE

Pleasure barges lie still
    along the quiet quay.
Arched stone bridges
    jump across the River Seine.
From centuries past, paved pathways
    run along both its shores.
Early church bells toll
    from Saint Roch's towers.
The giant ferris wheel
    sits there, no longer turns.
Strollers, joggers, runners,
    glide by the Tulleries urns.
Contorted bronze figures
    on Alexander III's bridge pont,
stare across the gentle river too.

Eiffel's Tower, tall, magnificant,
    hovers above quiet streets, the rue.
Paris, a city renowned in my dreams,
    is now underfoot, as I cruise
    along both river banks.
I watch it flow like a magic stream,
    through the hearts of the French
    and first time visiting Yank.
Eastern skies now turn yellow, clean,
    popular trees on the sides glow green.
I stop and stare, light floods the scene,
    the sun rises over the River Seine.

A PARIS PARK AT FIVE AM

It is still
dark, the iron skeleton
of the open air market
stands screwed to cement tiles.
A plump Paris rat
scurries across the walk,
headed for the gutter
where crates of fresh fish
are stacked on ice.
Fountains are splashing,
flashing drops of water
on white marble slabs.
A green garbed street cleaner
with his power washer
hoses off the sidewalk,
flushing pigeon droppings
and fresh dog poop
into the street.
A gendairme hustles off
a reluctant drunk,
roused from deep slumber
on his concrete park bench.
His companion urinates
against a plane tree,
ridding himself
of too much last night's wine.
A car roars by,
cracking the Boulevard sound barrier.
Shops are closed, barred,
graffiti decorates garage doors.
Parked cars line the streets,
straddling the crosswalks,
camped out on sidewalks
and both sides of one way streets.
The city's pulse is slow,
it is almost dead.
Then a flurry of activity starts,
vendors set up fruit stands,
tables are piled high with vegetables,
fish is placed on iced styrofoam.
The gray sky lightens,
pedestrians appear magically,
and another busy Paris day
is about to break wide open.

THE ARC D' TRIUMPHE

Fresh flowers are laid near the flame,
a dozen boulevards converge like spokes
to the hub of a huge stone arch.
Created to celebrate Napoleon's wars,
he was dead before it was done.
Triumphant allied forces on parade
at the end of the war to end all wars
beneath the arched circle of marble.
Nazi's goose-stepped through the portal,
thousands died before the rumble stopped.
Sculptures hewed from quiet stone,
portray man's ideals, his highest thoughts.
Circular steps, innumberable to count,
reach upward to the open top crown.
Climbing, one step at a time, up I go,
emerging breathless on its terrace.
I gasp at the all encompassing view,
a stiff wind whips through my hair.
Paris lies far below at my feet,
trees line boulevards with greenry.
People below are mere specks,
cars crawl like tiny bugs on streets below.
Arc d' Triumphe, rising like a sphinx
above one of the world's great cities,
holds the tomb of an unknown soldier.

arc de Triomphe de l'Étoile - PARIS

PARIS BEGGARS

An unkempt man, far gone
in the throes of too much wine,
shakes his tin cup
for more booze money.
An aged lady sits on the steps
of St. Roch's Church,
toothless, a pile of old rags
dumped there for a rummage sale.
A young Morrocan woman
croons to her sleeping baby,
draped like a blanket
across her lap as she sits
on the sidewalk in front
of the souvenir shop.
A supposedly blind man slumps
with his white cane
across his knees, shoes
worn and battered
from walking the asphalt streets.
Shouting unintelligible French,
he enters one door of the Metro car,
works his way through the crowd
and exits through the rear
at the next scheduled stop.
With acne pocked face
among his straggly thin hair,
a worn out man smells
like last week's garbage
as he sits in the gutter.
Like a floating spectre
rattling his tin cup,
another dares me to enter
Notre Dame without paying.
A mother sends out her two kids
to work the block
with castoff MacDonald cups.
One lays on the sidewalk,
too spent to even move,
wool cap placed in a strageic
spot to receive spare coins.
Another speaks a strange tongue,
then moves off to find
a more vulnerable target.
Each works the trade
in a special way,
eking out a living, I suppose,
or a dying in Paris, the city
with perhaps a generous heart.

DRIVING IN THE STREETS OF PARIS

Wide boulevards, crowded speedways,
narrow cobbled streets, over parked.
Many, many signs, in a foreign language,
roundabouts, darting pedestrians, pietons.
Long stop lights, short tempers,
honking horns, silent yellow signals.
Street sweepers, piles of trash,
few gas stations, many parks.
Old buildings, modern trucks,
neoned restaurants, closed on Monday banks.
Boulangeries, patissieres,
laveries, brassieres, bouchieres,
hotel du ville, Cirque d' Hiver.
Placa Bastille, rue de Republic,
River Siene, jardins and tulleries.
Around the block, one way again,
creative parking, motor scooters.
Weaving cyclists, dark tunnels,
speeding Renaults, wandering tourists.
Payant parking, ten francs an hour,
unleashed dogs, fresh brown poop.
Narrow lanes, cutting in and out,
blocked crosswalks, double parking.
Helpless gendairmes, taxis galore,
a jumble of humanity, it's a jungle out there!

EIFFEL TOWER

Like a giant spider,
your four iron legs
hold onto the ground.
Your angled concrete slabs
hold fast to these feet,
before the calves curve up
to meet as one slender shaft.
Rivets and bolts,
placed one at a time years ago,
are now painted gray,
iron criss-crossing
in abstract lines, forms.
Elevators climb your legs,
carrying crowds of tourists,
heavenward toward your peak.
Huge wheels turn slowly,
steel cables are wrapped around
spools of woven wire webs.
Swift elevators whisk
stunned spectators aloft.
At your third stage platform,
far above the soaring pigeons,
I gaze in awe at the Paris city.
Boulevards of green radiate
while the winding River Siene
threads its away among the white
buildings, the far away streets.
Buses, trucks are like ants,
people disappear in the distance,
the wind blows cold from the west.
I feel a world away in your arms.
You are an engineering marvel,
you stand your sentinel post,
watching over the jungle people.
You may lift them from their strife,
they can raise their eyes to you.
Oh, Eiffel Tower, long may you stand
a symbol, a beacon for man's quest.

LES CHATEAUX

In the heart of France
where the Loire, the Cher and Indre meet,
are castles of my dreams.
Perched upon green wooded hills,
stones piled up from yesteryear,
are fashioned into galleries, walls.
Towers and spires poke the air,
above where kings and dukes
built palaces for vanity's sake alone.
Great hunting lodges, chateaus,
graced the dark forests growing there.
Backs of peasants, serfs were bent,
artisans created objects d' art
for their royalty, kings and queens.
Moats, high walls, ramparts,
kept out the enemy. Now picturesque,
they are open to the common folk.

Cars, buses, bikes, unknown to kings,
carry the curious tourist
through places of former opulence.
Tapestries, faded by time's own bleach,
deck the cold stone walls inside.
Paintings, with captured faces
of ancient courtesans, still hang there.
Carved cabinets, intricate in design,
are stared at in wonderment.
Marble stairs once tread by royal feet,
carry everyone up toward heaven's roof.

We now live free of disease, the plague,
which carried off blue bloods too.
No longer do we watch in horror
as royal heads are chopped off in public.
Liberty means all are free to live
and move in glorious castles on the river.
In our day, romantic kings are fantasized,
ancient knights remain chivalrous,
and princesses are forever beautiful.
Yet, it is we who are privileged now.
These lovely old castles, chateaus,
tell us that once only a few were best.
Now, everyone who walks these halls,
are kings and queens with the rest.

JB-97

mehun-s-Yèvre Ruins
- Class II Keep -

39

ST. ROCH

In the dark medieval days,
   when bubonic plague swept the earth,
      there lived in France a humble duke named Roch.

He gave up his governing,
   and cared for those afflicted with the pestilence,
      traveling from place to place, caring for the sick.

He spent three years at this,
   made a pilgrimage to Rome on their behalf,
      but alas, he himself soon had the dreaded sores.

His life was burning low,
   a faithful dog licked his wounds, brought him bread,
      and as legend has it, he was cured.

Once again he went about doing good,
   where ever saw human need,
      he cared for the sick and dying.

So when ever you see pictures of a Saint,
   with his dog carrying a loaf of bread,
      you know it must be St. Roch, who cared.

JB-97   Jeanne d'Arc TOWER - ROUEN

THE ROSE OF SAINT BRIGET

In a large cathedral in France,
I speak of Notre Dame of Amiens,
are many iron gated chapels.
Nestled among those pillars of stone,
lighted by radiant stained glass rainbows,
is a dusty quiet place of worship.
The massive organ sounds a fugue,
a priest sings his mass out loud.
With strangers, tourists, I wander about,
marveling at the distant ceiling arches,
pointed Gothic, far above the floor stones.
Carved wooden figures from ancient days,
reside upon the choir stalls.
Placques are fastened to rocky walls,
telling of lives lost in the world's wars.
Words commemorate those fighting men
who struggled and died upon the soil
that surrounds this great church.
Guilded golden statuary stands still
with Biblical chiseled scenes in stone
painted with polychrome and dust.

In one aisle along the awesome nave,
I find a small quiet chapel,
dedicated to Saint Briget herself.
A dark oil painting hangs there,
her radiant face the only spot of light.
No candles are lit in this desolate place,
no one stands there in reverent prayer.
Yet, I see thrust upon its iron gate,
a wilting, solitary red rose flower.
Its stem is a dry green brown,
the deep red petals are fading fast.
The bloom hangs its head in shame,
crucified upon the wrought iron frame.
Who placed their love upon these black bars?
Who called Saint Briget in silent prayer?

JB-92

Perhaps it is I who call her now,
as I walk by the crypts and tombs.
I watch the dying rose hanging there,
even as my own life fades away.
Saint Briget, hear my own mortal cry,
even as this lovely rose dries,
let my own spirit with you rise.

LA CHAUME

Among the maize and wheat,
down the road from fields of rape seed
and acres of carrots gone to flower,
sits an ancient farmhouse, La Chaume.
A barnyard is found outback
with tractors, mowers, reapers,
and a modern sailboat too.
Garfon, the large lab dog,
his brown tail stump wagging,
meets the weary traveler
at the end of the narrow road.
A gray black donkey brays
from his pen back of the B&B,
while yapping hunting dogs frolic.
An aged water pump with rusty wheels
once drawing water up by hand,
rests upon a green knoll
in the middle of a graveled yard.
Barn swallows flit in and out,
their mud plastered nests
cling to the massive barn beams.
Tiny heads peep out from holes,
white breasts fly across the drive,
while insects perish by the thousands.
Wild red poppies line road ditches,
crows flap and caw across the fields.
Quail run, flutter, then fly
through the green sunflower stalks
whose yellow bonnets follow the sun.
This farm has a Cote d' hote,
a place to withdraw from the world.
With simple French bread, peach jam
and fresh milk from the dairy,
one's weary body can eat
and sleep in peace.

At La Chaume, the happy hosts
make one feel at home.
Bent and broken spinning wheel
tells of traditions from the past.
Writing tables, chairs, couches,
allow the traveler to rest.
Ah, La Chaume, how we yearn
for your simple daily life.
How we miss your beauty,
your friendliness, your charm.
Wherever we may go from here,
we will always remember you,
the French farm, La Chaume.

Une pompe du puits

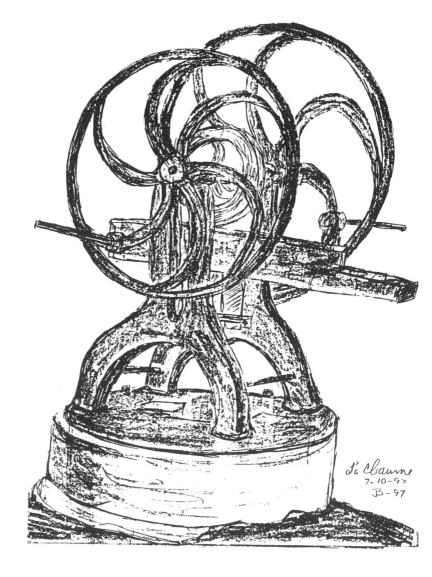

La Claume
7-10-97
B-97

46

SUNFLOWERS IN FRANCE

Rolling hills are patched
with golden yellow fields
of sun flowers, facing
the early morning sun.
Vine yards in rows
of deep summer green,
have unripe grapes
hanging hidden there.
Fields of maize or corn,
are a lush verdant hue,
with a touch of autumn brown.
A jack rabbit hops
across the narrow road,
a fly buzzes overhead.

I stop and gaze
upon a large golden disk,
encircled with a halo
of bright yellow petals.
The green-brown center
with developing seeds,
host crawling bees and bugs.
A ring of stubby hairs
surround the insects
plate like meeting place.

Light green stalks
twist and turn magically
to follow Apollo
across the summer sky.
Heart shaped leaves
of deepest green,
send nourishment to the head.

The sunflower looks back at me,
its simple face seems a smile.
God has created this marvelous plant,
and allows me to know its beauty.

48

THE OLD MILL IN BRETAGNE

Four hundred years have long since passed
when its stone walls were laid upon the grass.
Rocks mortared with long lasting lime,
look fresh and new after so long a time.
Rough wooden wheel with turning teeth,
dips into the running mill race beneath.
Around and around it turns endlessly,
pushed by the falling water relentlessly.
Its moss covered slats have often been replaced,
and still the raw wood on stone is based.

Gray rock walls are pierced with squares
of red shuttered windows which open there.
Gutter spouts carry the rain straight down
from its shake shingle roof above the town.
White lichens, green moss, spot its walls,
trunks of massive oaks line the water falls.
Sparrows and swallows chirp away,
singing their songs on a summer day.
Crystal water tumbles from its river source,
to flat lily pads which lie on the water course.

A gentle summer breeze cools the air,
stone flower boxes hold rainbows there.
The murmur of quiet water is heard,
adding its melody to the singing birds.
A white heron now fishes the shallow stream,
and rustic wooden bridges add to the scene.
Honey bees buzz those colored blooms,
making our bread sweet in the dining room.
Boulders, now sprinkled with flowers,
line the river bank, hold up the axel power.

The massive mill wheel still turns around,
corn, wheat seeds there once were ground.
Tons of water have slapped its angled flaps,
spinning and turning thousands of laps.
Other poets have languished here,
watching the spokes turn slowly near.
So many seasons have the willows wept,
while shading the walls where the ivy crept.
Many wanderers through Bretagne go,
stop and gaze at this old mill slough.

It is here at this millside that I learn,
that time never stops, it always turns.
May these words tell others what has been,
as mighty wheel, I watch you spin.

MONT ST. MICHEL

The cry of the seagull echoes across the bay,
a strong westerly wind whips the flags.
Towering over the tidelands of the Atlantic,
is a solid rock island, with a man made
crown of cathedral that reaches heavenward.
A causeway, crowded with autos, trucks,
all trying to escape the incoming tide,
runs to the shore two kilometers away.

A fire red glow from the setting sun,
soon dies, extinguished by a cold Atlantic rain,
like a campfire squelched by falling water.
A woman sits huddled in her own lawn chair,
whipped by the cold piercing wind,
facing the holy site in reverence,
she doesn't move, like a modern statue.
Bicycles are strapped a locked,
owners pass into the medieval walls.
The weathered stone of the ancient abbey,
turns sienna brown as spot lights
beam upon its slender pointed spires.

The tide slowly rises, then rushes in,
soon covering parking lots, polder grass.
Towering Mount St. Michel becomes an island,
its thousand years are like a day.
Tides rush in, then fall away again,
man walks the stone paths up the hill.
Oh, beautiful Mount St. Michel,
you call all of us to come home again.

LOST IN LANGUEDOC

The directions are simple enough,
follow the D-4 route, cross D-18 and up the hill.
Small French towns with stuccoed walls,
all seem the same in the evening sun.
The route signs just disappear,
across the railroad tracks,
D-4 vanishes into the plein air.
Through canopied plane tree lanes,
by bright sunflower fields
and vineyards with hanging grapes,
we wander through the dusk.

Like a carousel that goes round and round,
we return to the centre ville square.
Natives speak only in excited tongue,
"dorite" or "schuss" or "viola"
which makes to sense to us.
To Montaban, Vors, or Ste Ceale d' Aves,
we have again traveled too far.
A mystery Castel-de-Montmichal
is never found, nor can we find
signs for Toulet or Vors or what.
The golden rays of the setting sun
disappear behind the darkened hills.
Dark roads, homes without lights,
shuttered farms and vicious dogs,
discourage any further query.

Upon the corner of a queer cross road,
we see a small white house.
A cheery light gleams from its door,
lighted lamp glows in the driveway.
A hesitant knock upon that door,
brings friendly faces to our aid.
Reading our letter of instructions,
with exclamations and discussions,
the man of the house gives us the sign.
We follow him and his family
through the dark countryside
with its wild and lonely lanes.

We soon arrive at the Mas du Sudre,
our bed and breakfast for the night.
With a hug and handshake, we part,
from those helpful, friendly French folk.

Maps may help tell people where they be,
but it is friendly strangers
who really know where we are.
We are never lost when others share
their territory and their loving care.

RIVER VEREZE

Your dark still waters do not ripple.
The morning sky turns pink and gray
over the banks of the quiet Vereze.

Your banks are lush with growing summer trees.
Willows are weeping at the river side,
ducks are fluffing up their feathers.

An ancient stone wall channels your flow.
Water courses silently below bridge arches,
geese preen their tails upon the shore.

Cows are resting by your side, chewing cuds of grass.
The stream meanders by their pasture,
a narrow cow path takes me there.

You wind your way along with a quiet murmur.
Here in the Valley of the Vereze,
pre-historic man painted art in caves.

You saw man began to reason here, to think, to love.
Along these winding verdant banks,
ancient man began to walk upright.

You watched him capture fire, slay wild beasts.
It was along this water course,
man first left for us his art.

Slowly, flowing Vereze, you pass by like time.
I stop and gaze at your handiwork,
then move again upon my way.

MONTAGNE DU LUBERON

A purple mist hovers on ragged crown
of the mighty mountains of Luberon.
It rises from lavender carpets
that deck the valley floor far below.
Glowing in rows of sweet perfume,
they are enhanced by a summer's rain.
These flowers offer up their violet fragrance
to the amber early morning sky.

The summer's long gray dawn,
slowly turns yellow in the east.
Sharp stony crags reflect the light,
dark trees ring the massive base.
A meadow lark sings it melody
that echoes across fields of blooms.
Wayward thistle along the roadside
hurls its pointed stars of purple too.

Indigo peaks of Luberon's ridges
stretch across a rugged and wild scene.
Clear springs tumble which once quenched
the thirst of roaming Romans.
Stone terraces cling precariously to cliffs,
wildflowers spring up in tiny cracks.
I stand in awe at Nature's handiwork,
lavender fields amid white rock walls.

The yellow flame of early sun,
rises quickly above us all.
It glides across wild Luberon
where wolves once danced and howled.
Oh, purple mountains, fields of lavender,
you have captured my heart, my all.

CATHEDRAL WINDOWS

Rainbow jewels sparkle from the sun,
St. Etienne's gothic windows glow.
Biblical tales etched in glass,
are mounted in thirteenth century stone.
Its soaring arches, flying buttresses,
leap far above the dazzled eye.
Inside, the silence of the sacred place,
echoes light beams from leaded glass.
Crypts, chapels, apse, all gleam in color,
petitioner's candles flicker in the dark.
The walls of this saintly tomb,
are perforated with kaleidoscopes.
Bishops and archbishops bones
lie there bathed in heavenly light.

I tread the well worn floor marbles,
pillars reach heavenward toward the sky.
A huge wooden pipe organ sings
of ancients who built this church.
I gasp and stare in quiet awe,
at the magnificance before me.
Unable to speak what my heart says,
my mouth is mute, my eyes overflow.

Oh, you who have passed this way before,
did you see reds mix with yellows, blacks?
Has the broken prism light fallen
and illuminated your unspoken quest?
Did you watch the blues and greens
harmonize with ochres and oranges?
Have the shattered rainbows fallen
on you from these glowing windows?
Did the marvels of St. Etienne's glass
change your life as it has mine?

SUNDAY AFTERNOON IN THE PARK

Bois de Boulogne sounds so romantic
like a French king's hunting ground.
In Bagetelle (a part of B de B),
a beautiful chateaux sits nestled
among the trees, the walks, the flowers.
Orange trees line the graveled paths,
winter's freeze would kill them
except their wooden pots and tubs
are brought inside the Orangerie.

It is summer now, the orange trees
are outside, blooming, bearing fruit.
The vacant winter abode is empty,
except for rows of chairs, a stage.
A grand piano waits in anticipation
with its slanted lid wide open
like a baby bird waiting for the worm.
Formal gardens of roses, yellow, white,
red, purple, orange, any color you name,
lie like a carpet before the windows.
People stroll the white aisles of gravel,
from the green gazebo on the hill
to the shaped, pruned green trees.
A few wander into the Orangerie
and soon the seats are full.

A black tuxed announcer, sweating
in the blistering Paris August heat,
introduces the chamber music group.
Sweet strains of Beethoven's music
soon drifts across the manicured lawns.
A lively Brahms' clarinet concerto
and his quintet for strings
fill the air with royal music.

Kings and Queens, Dukes and Duchesses
once lolled here to hear these notes,
these compositions made for the court.
Yet, on this Sunday afternoon,
a poor farm boy from America
can thrill to the same music,
the same lush jardins, flowers,
once reserved only for kings.

French hunting horns trumpet the arrival of
Tchaikovsky's Fourth and I watch the violas play
hide and seek between the conductor's arms and legs.
Meanwhile, the basses grab the fingers of their
masters, pull them across their exposed strings.
I stare at two harps rocking back and forth, angels
plucking their transparent faces, searching for
beautiful zits. The slender oboe lifts its tiny
nasal twang in harmony with the shrill cry of the
silvered flute. The lanky bassoon croons a rich song
from deep within its wooden soul and sends B flats
down my spine.

A chorus of violins wave their arms in mass
synchronism, dancing to their choreographer's white
baton. I gaze at the cellos, who without shame,
nestle their naked bodies between the legs of men
dressed in motorcycle black. Mellow cries of joy
come from the bows stroking their vibrating strands
of hair. Descending marbled musical steps, the black
clarinet lays its plaintive cloak upon the sliding
trombone's polished bannister. Wind winds its way
through the tuba's labyrinth.

Incessant rhythms rattle my empty skull and
harmonies strum my taut heart strings. Symphonic
sounds bounce off those bowling balls in the rows
ahead of me and beat upon a drum within my chest.
When rumbling kettles and mated cymbals announce
the end of this musical orgy, my own clapping hands
blend into a prolonged musical ovation.

POEMS FROM NEW HAMPSHIRE
AND OTHER PLACES

JB -97

MAILBOX

Its wooden post is slightly askew.
A rusting mailbox,
approved by the Postmaster General,
sits quietly upon the helm.
The top is reddish brown with rust,
its red signal flag droops down.
The silent trees, distant hills
speak reverently
to this sentinel.
On a fading white, turning gray,
emblazoned in purest black
are the owner's name,
R. FROST.

DANCING WITH THE BIRCHES

Old feet are shoe clad with heel-worn Reeboks,
wet ribbed sox slide down ancient ankles.
A red colored T-shirt turns dark with sweat,
it's tucked and set into blue boxer running shorts.
A hazy New Hampshire morning sun
struggles to rise above the mountains, hills,
tired legs plod up the steep rural road,
jogging slowly in the forest shadow's dark wake.
Tall white pines, hemlocks, stretch toward the sky,
maples fan their verdant leaves in a lazy breeze.
A wild rabbit hops and scurries across the roadway,
then disappears into a field of new mown hay.
A dog barks in the distance, a robin bounces
across the yard while an old frog jumps
into a roadside ditch.
            Young birches spring up beside,
waving their dark branches along the jogging trail,
while others change their trunks from brown to white.
Sawtoothed leaves flicker and shimmer in the light,
a soft wind rises with low whisper, quiet murmur,
and the tender birch limbs began to dance and sway.
They tremble and move to some silent music
lean away or bunch together in crowded pairs.
Chalk white trunks with rings and lines of black
seem to promenade in the summer wood.
            A new lightness pulses in tired legs,
breath comes easier and mind fog clears with the mist.
The worn out human machine seems overhauled
as it runs and dances with the birches.

THE POET'S TRAIL

A path sidles gently up
the New Hampshire hill,
threads its way among the grass
and disappears among maples,
white birches and towering pines.
Inside this curtain
of sticks and trunks,
the way leads upwards
between moss covered granite,
fallen branches and hunks
of slimey muck.
Black decaying leaves
form a walkway for my halting steps
and an orange creeping slug.
An ancient woodpile
lies abandoned there,
stacked, forgotten, cast aside
by a woodsman whose saw
has long since been still.

Half moon fungus grows
in striped tan, multiple rows,
upon trees felled by wind or hand.
They now return by rotting
to their mountain soil
from which they once sprung.
Mosquitoes float like wisps of smoke,
a woodpecker hammers on a tree.
While the trees are decked
in deepest summer green,
a few red jewels
of early turned maple leaves
shimmer and dance upon the trail.
The dark mud oozes
where trickling hillside water
wanders across the path.

An imprinted cast in this mud
of a human heel and shoe,
tells of another poet
who once strolled among the ferns.
He sat upon the moss rocks,
the soft carpeted stumps,
and stopped at this quiet place.
This cathedral floor beneath
giant pines was once walked
by a poet who contemplated
the clearing made by saw and axe.
He looked at tumbled trees too,
all down like a game of pick-up-sticks.
He heard the cry of the crow,
felt the early morning fog,
marveled at distant mountain peaks.
Some future poets may come this way,
and may they blend their spirits
with mine and Robert Frost's.

PEMIGEWASSET RIVER

Tumbling from the old White Mountains,
where granite man peers out,
falls the clear brown waters of the Pemigewasset.
Each spring, New Hampshire's melting snow
transforms this quiet brook
into a raging menace, a thundering cascade.
Uprooting trees, shoving rocks
and logs aside like feathers,
the upward path beside it
is strewn with debris, wasted trees.
Summer hikers marvel at the tangled webs
of bared roots, clinging to muddy banks.
A rainbow of oaks and maples,
hemlocks too, hide its singing waters
flowing and trickling down in autumn.
With winter's fog and flying snow,
ice cakes the quiet pools.
Near the bottom lies a hallowed out basin
where water's diamond saw twists and falls,
swirls, rushes, eons of sculpting hardest stone.
The Old Man's Foot treads upon a ledge,
where hollyberries gleam red upon the green,
and roars the thunder of the plunging stream.
One comes by this natural place but once,
its magic touches the failing heart,
and tired legs may never climb
again its bouldered course.

DAHLIAS

Round balls of petaled flowers
perch upon their slender stalks,
gleam with white or deep purple power,
in the sun during my early morning walks.
Saw toothed leaves, tuberous hidden roots,
nourish balls of beauty for my eager eyes.
Bees tread with pollen laden boots
upon stems of green and purple which rise.
Each petal is curved with perfect essence,
all made perfectly just the same.
With each flower, there is a presence
so anyone can readily say your name.
Dahlias growing beautifully in the dell,
you show Nature's plan so lovely and well.

THE HAWK AND THE HARE

On Kinsman Ridge Road, a summer afternoon,
a long tailed hawk swooped and swerved.
Landing on a tree limb above my head,
its hooked beak menaced below fierce eyes.
Traveling further along that gravel trail,
a brown wild rabbit hopped across the road.
Glancing momentarily at my advancing form,
it disappeared into the roadside underbrush.

Did my tread upon that rural road
spare the life of that doomed hare?
Did I rob nature of the hawk's feast
or was the hare itself too quick and fast?

I TOOK A BATH

IN BENNY GOODMAN'S TUB

In the Cinnamon Room, resides an ancient bath tub,
reported by experts to be Benny Goodman's own.
Stretching six feet from rear to drain,
in it, I could swim laps all alone.
Its gold plated faucets stood guard on the floor,
cracked porcelain handles lay flat on their heads.
One was marked "H" and the other "C",
that's what the Roman letters said.
A center post with its own knobby dome,
some magic invention that seemed unique,
had a golden collar upon copper shoulders,
an unknown, unnamed, useless antique.
A golden globe spout let the water in
while a rubber plug stopped up the hole.
A soap dish hung upon its enameled lip,
with slippery stuff, shampoo, which I stole.
The porcelain pitcher upon its wooden stand
was used to baptize my head, wet my hair.
Wash rags scrubbed, rinse water too away,
sweat, skin, germs, foul body odor in the air.
While sitting there, soaking in that giant tub,
I listened for the music of Benny's dance parade.
The runs and shrill of his clever clarinet
blended with the steady saga of my Goodman charade.
It made my toes and feet tread upon the water,
I thrilled to bathe in the tub where Benny slept.
Even after toweling off, combing back my hair,
I still could not play that clairvoyant clarinet.

WORK HORSES

Three huge horses, tall and tan,
stand at the corner of the pasture land,
their friendly ochre faces munching grass.
They lift their massive feet and sway,
stomp and tramp the fresh mown hay,
standing like statues from the past.
Light manes ripple, flow from sturdy necks,
nuzzle one another, stand close and flick
flies from muscled haunches, strong backs.
An artist sits beside the country road,
her easel dabbed with its oil paint load,
admiring these beasts as if cast in wax.
She tries to capture their strength, power
upon her small flimsy canvas tower,
while they swish their broom tails all day.
Perhaps they are thinking of late last night
when they pulled a loaded wagon so light,
full of squealing, singing youth and hay.
Babbling teenagers nestled among the straw,
enthralled by horses in their moonlight awe,
like those times from long years before.
Perhaps they are standing there and dream
of drinking cool water from a nearby stream,
or sleeping in clean stalls with soft floors.
Maybe they yearn for a grooming of their coats,
or from autumn's harvest, a bucket of oats,
or a lump of sugar from their master.
Whether harnessed each day to pull their load
along a dusty New Hampshire country road,
or running free in fields or pasture,
these giant work horses are quiet and serene.
They accept their lot in Nature's scheme,
whether standing still or trotting faster.

BROTHERS

Along a rural New Hampshire road
stands a twisted tamarack tree.
Its trunk is strong and sturdy
yet its body is deformed, misshapened.
The crown and heart of it,
once its beauty and true core,
have been trimmed and cut out
so a power line can course on through.
Its arms sag down to the ground,
others stretch for the sky.
A small sign is tacked on its trunk,
"650" speaks from its rugged bark.

Nearby is a slim, barkless power pole,
its creosote base planted in the earth.
A white transformer box hangs rigid,
nodding its head from near the top.
Once a living pine, tall and straight,
it now holds the electric, telephone lines.
It sends out its charged black wire
towards the warped tamarack tree.
The strings and lines running straight,
seem to bind the two trees together.
Different brothers, one alive and deformed,
the other handsome, clean but forever dead.

SONNET TO A RHODODENDRON

Your evergreen leaves hold clumps of various hues,
gorgeous bells ring silently of spring's good news.
Tall trees or just bushes of lavender pink,
you swarm on hillsides, crowd cliffs at their brink.
Your tender petals, balls of red, blaze for days,
setting on fire dark green forest pathways.
Rain bathes your limbs laden with white blooms,
hot sun bursts buds on your woven branch looms.
When May slides into the month of June,
your flowers wither, the rainbow ends too soon.
Your velvet clusters wilt, shrivel, as they must,
great heads of color fade and fall away to dust.
Your bunches of beauty disappear from sight,
truth hides in another long summer's night.

A WINTER AFTERNOON

From their carpet of dried brown grass,
yellow dandelions reflect the low winter sun.
Some have turned into white puffed balls,
matching floating fleecy clouds above.
A cold evening breeze blows across the playground,
where cries of early childhood delight
echo from a bright orange plastic slide.
Picnic tables and stone benches are empty,
too cold for beer, sandwiches or potato chips.
Trash barrels are empty too, plastic liners
poised to receive summer's excess surplus.
Long shadows of trees fall across my page,
their empty twigs and dormant buds,
push my thoughts, my yearnings,
and my pen toward poems of spring.

RESIDENT HALLS

In summer, the halls are long and empty,
but short and full with the new semester.
Now no boitrous laughs echo down the hall,
during this break, running legs do not fly at all.
My door key sounds like a rifle shot
as the dead bolt falls away,
a slamming door could be a cannon roar,
decibels splitting apart the corridor.

Where have all the students gone,
to surf, to farm, to shovel or to snore?
Where are all the skulls and brains
to float in these empty streets?
Will empty heads who traverse these ways
be filled with knowledge and wisdom
when autumn leaves begin to fall?

Just a stranger sitting here all alone,
I wonder about the lives and hopes
of those who will sleep, then study,
or play along these hallowed halls.

WRITING TANKAS

The wooden lamp stand
holds an incadescent bulb.
Power through the cord,
illuminates my study
as I write these tanka poems.

THE TOWN THAT WOKE UP

Along the banks of the Kalamazoo
River near Battle Creek,
is a sleepy little town that woke up.
An Interstate rubbed its borders,
a MacDonalds and Burger King
sprouted like mushrooms on its edge.
Self-serve Shell and Marathon stations
serve the steady stream of cars
on north thirty-fifth street.
A new Pizza King with bright red tables
clash with new sidewalks
along Michigan Avenue downtown.
Several mini-strip malls
have scarred the quaint village face.
A new high school, in a cow pasture,
matches the modern red brick
municipal center and three police cars.
The new three stop lights
slow the traffic from speeding
by the Gale-Valley Estates
R-V park nearby. Oak trees
are trimmed to let power lines go by,
school buses stop to pick up kids
who no longer can walk a mile.
A lone woman stands on a street corner
smoking her cigarette
while the United Methodist Church
is waiting next to the funeral home.
An indoor heated flea market
replaces the old antique store,
a plaster cow in someone's front yard
replaces the real ones out back.
An amublance fleet sits ready
to answer the emergency call,
the cars whiz by so fast,
it isn't safe for dogs anymore.

The town is awake,
homes are filled with computers,
appliances, Video stores flourish.
The goldfinches and cardinals
are bewildered or have moved away.
Deer no longer rummage
through the vegetable gardens,
rabbits have migrated to the country.
Misquitoes do not buzz around
on a warm summer's night,
owls do not hoot at midnight.
Neighbors don't know each other,
porches are now passe'.
The small village of Galesburg
has awakened, but somehow
it still seems almost dead.

THE TIDE IS GOING OUT

The tide is going out,
and the rough pockmarked rocks,
on which gray barnacles cling,
are jumbled into random piles.
Rolling waves turn themselves into surf
which batters the beach boulders
and sends white tongues licking
the tide pools around my feet.
Black mussels perch in salty pockets,
with their fetid stagnant water
trickling back down the damp rocks
as rivulets heading towards the sea.
A fisherman casts his reel
into the pounding crashing surf,
waiting for some unwary one
to snap at its hooked tender morsel.

Even as the yellow sun ball falls,
a ruler straight horizon line
separates the dark gray water
from the late afternoon winter sky.
A square flat freighter
hides its form in the dusk,
and Catalina Island looms
dragon like through the distant haze.
Shoreline cliffs are decked
in olive green winter grass,
with sienna streaks of rock
poking eons of strata into view.
Stones, ground round by the ocean
lay scattered upon the shore,
waiting for another incoming tide
to polish them smooth some more.

The sky gradually glows yellow,
then orange, as the color wheel turns
towards red and a deep purple hue
of the coming long dark night.
The tide goes out and the water's low,
yet spray splashes across my page
and a cold breeze sends shivers
up and down my ancient aching back.
A brown pelican roosts upon a rock,
while the cry of a soaring gull,
seeking a place to rest the night,
pierces my lonely silent shell.
Umber clouds hover over the scene,
and the evening sun bites the horizon.
It soon rapidly sinks out of sight
below the ocean's dark gray ripples.
My spirits disappear with the fallen sun,
the black night sky is empty now.
There are no bright stars to fill the void,
my life rushes out with the evening tide.

STONE LOVE SEAT

A stone love seat sits high
on a bluff above the Iowa River,
its view blocked by growing trees
with trunks the size of a runner's thigh.
Embedded in the old concrete side
is "L.A. Class - 1914."
Built solid for heavy sparking,
generations of necking, petting,
and social intercourse
have not yet worn it out.
The wide brown river flows
silently by, its murmur still
listening to the same low voices.
What dreams, aspirations, or life plans
have been formed, changed, discussed
by those who sat upon its throne.

The ancient stone sits there quietly,
a monument to another time
when automobiles did not rush by,
horses trotted along the river bank,
and students trudged through the snow.
The adjacent President's House
is a red brick color of autumn leaves,
built long after the bench appeared.

Down the river, rolling farms
still wave their fields of corn
across the deep plowed prairies.
Damp green moss clings
to the sturdy base as it did years before,
young lovers still stroll and sit
upon the cold and massive bench.
They hold hands, explore hearts and minds,
or just gaze into each others eyes.
This isolated and lonely monument
resides upon that college hill,
where mixed and fixed in its cement,
it tells its tale of love and learning.

STRATHMORE

Today, I went running
in the Strathmore mountains,
Toscaninni led me there.
From Mt. Palomar Place,
I could see far below,
across Mt. Whitney Way, where
Mt. Lassen Lane sparkled
with night street lights glow.
The chill of early morning,
sped me along Mt. Sawtooth Drive
and I soon cruised on by
Mt. Langley Court, just as
sunrise clouds were forming.
Saddleback lay shrouded
in far distant eastern mists,
and sprinklers were shooting water
where ever Mt. Vancouver went.
Lining the gray asphalt still,
suburban houses were silent,
on Mt. Hood's quiet hill.
I huffed up Mt. Rushmore Road,
my heart was beating fast,
but then my tired legs coasted
down Mt. Ranier's slope at last.
Mt. Shasta was long and smooth,
and I soon jogged on past
Mt. Rose's fragrant blooms.
I stumbled down the final hill
on Bloomwood Road, no worse,
until I met Amelia,
and she turned my course.
Today, I seem to still be roaming
among those Strathmore mountains,
which are not too far from home.

MY HOMETOWN

Fifty years have sped by
since I rode my bike down
South Clay Street, Nottawa,
jogged along Centerville Road.
The old high school
is now a middle school,
demoted and stuffed
with computers, larger classrooms.
The gym, were basketball games,
operettas, graduations, bacculareates
were community events,
had the old stage
all bricked up,
the floor refinished
and bleachers replaced.
The cafeteria moved to the library,
study hall was abolished,
the library migrated
to the art room.
The principal's office is gone,
and so is he. The grass covered
playground is asphalt,
the obstacle course is oblivion,
cloak rooms are replaced by lockers.

The Citizen's Bank
where I started a college
savings account still stands
on the main corner
at Nottawa and Chicago Road.
The President of the Bank,
just died a month or so ago
and my savings vanished
many moons ago.
The Crusader Arms Rooming House
is now a fancy restaurant,
the Old Hotel transformed
into Sigrist's Furniture Store.

Family Barbers, where I shined shoes,
is still there, giving out haircuts
but for more than two bits.
The shoe shine stand is gone,
and Fogelsong's Funeral Home
has changed its name.
David's Drive In Dairy Bar
has turned from white to brown,
some other business owns the ground.

Spence Field, where baseball, track
and football once were played,
is now home of slow pitch softball
and horseshoe pits
for white haired atheletes.

My quiet hometown
has enlarged its girth also.
Fast food places on the outskirts,
rumbling trucks down the main drag,
the Carnegie Library is a gas station.
The Daily Journal newspaper has moved,
the hospital spreads out its wings.
The Bottling Works, M&R factory,
Burr Oak Tool and Die have changed,
only memories now remain.
Fires, storms, progress itself
has changed my boyhood home.
Even with the passing years,
I can still only see it
as it once was, a long time ago.

SUNRISE OVER NORTHERN INDIANA

From the neighbor's coop,
    a rooster sings his duet
    with the "Beep-beep-beep" music
    of a backing up monster
    landfill machine.
Their harmony rings
    across the Valley of Land Fills,
    over corn planted fields
    and acres of soybeans.
The cattle feed lot stench
    pierces the summer air,
    mixes with the aroma
    of landfill from the west.
Lush, belt high corn
    marches in stiff rows
    while other stunted shoots
    struggle in baked clay.
In the east, lacy clouds
    filter the orange red sun,
    and barren tree limbs poke
    their stripped arms high.
Sweet peas pop delicate
    lavenders among roadside weeds,
    a stagnant black ditch
    holds discarded bottles, cans.
A lazy dirt road winds
    among verdant trees,
    while a cracked asphalt
    ribbon runs into town.
Black birds clatter
    and chatter their sweet song,
    a possum plays dead,
    another night's road kill.

Then a white tailed deer
　　bobs out of sight
　　as a battered old farm truck
　　rattles and creaks by.
Red winged blackbirds
　　perch on cattail reeds
　　in a pond, where old tires float,
　　sink in black mucky muck.
Acres of prime farmland,
　　once rich with corn,
　　transform into tracts,
　　developments, homes.
Unfenced fields
　　where rabbits once ran free
　　are now imprisoned
　　with hot barbed wire.
Trout Creek of boyhood
　　fishing fame
　　murmurs silently
　　through its cement culvert.
Ancient dirt roads
　　with two worn vehicle tracks
　　have been surfaced
　　and coated with asphalt tar.
Telephone poles and electric
　　overhead wires
　　are scrambled spaghetti
　　in the clear blue sky.
Nature's wonderland along the river St. Joe
is another victim of our modern life.

HAIKU

Green bamboo shoots poke
up from deep buried roots where
their ancestors sleep.

Soft clouds billow by
while clear skies change into gray
hair on a pillow.

Xylophone rumbles,
violin bow plays music
across my heart strings.

Picnic table stands,
swept clean by cold winter winds
and full waste basket.

Climbing ivy crawls
upon fence, around the ground,
beauty smothers all.

Sunlight, shade flickers,
wind rustles leaves, shadows dance,
deep roots are unmoved.

Rubber tree grows fat,
leaves thick, filled with bitter sap,
shade for neighbor's cat.

Baked potato skins,
turn golden with sweet butter,
buried under ground.

Walking in the sun,
waiting for stiff wind to stop,
I climb final hill.

Woodblock of lumber,
cut across the grain, planed smooth,
living sacrifice.

The sky is copper
over Saddleback Mountain,
lucky penny found.

The apricot tree
is blooming in the back yard.
It announces spring.

Bright star, untethered
in the sky, newspaper says
you're a satellite.

PARK CLOSED

The warped wood gate is shut, locked,
plowed snow is piled across the drive.
Two Colorado spruces stand there frocked
in blue green skirts on giant bee hives.
Embarrassed and naked bush branches poke
through their white winter earthern beds.
They dance with their fellow yellow stick folks,
waving a few dry leaves from vacant heads.
A gray squirrel flashes from its dark hole,
carved in an old oak tree from many years past.
Canada geese perch on the iron soccer poles,
dot the field, poking snow for their grass.
A black and white magpie flits by twice
like an infield hit across the diamond.
Bases are buried beneath drifts, frozen ice,
there are no fans to cheer, clap their hands.
A crushed rock bank is dusted white,
its yellow and red veins are cold, inert.
No foot tracks break the surface quite,
cars have not mangled the smooth white shirt.
A weathered wooden fence keeps me out,
as does a battered sign out there exposed.
Also neatly printed letters, without a doubt,
with its simple message, "Park is Closed."

BLANK VERSE

Pen lies on my desk
paper is blank without words.
My mind is vacant,
waiting for tankas to come,
then I'll quickly write them down.

84

PEOPLE POEMS

albert schweitzer - 1965

FOUR SENIORS ON THE BLUE LINE

His pure white hair rustles like a lion's mange
as the ticket machine spits out his dollar bill.
She fumbles in her purse for some loose change
which after insertion, tumbles down the reject till.
The electric train stops at Anaheim Station,
its doors fly open, people ooze onto the platform.
Both of the elderly patrons fizzle with frustration,
baffled by the stubborn automatic ticket form.
Unable to feed anymore money into the monster's maw,
they seem helpless victims of new technology pox.
Doors close, the train rumbles off. A voice caws
and startles them coming from a nearby metal box.
"Push the select button first," the speaker says,
"then put your money into the little slot!"
The "B" button is pushed, pounded in several ways,
and the machine quickly gobbles up their money lot.
Suddenly two tickets magically appear,
stamped and dated, passage is now allowed.
He pulls and strokes his sparse stringy beard,
she plucks out tickets and says, " For crying out loud!"

His crew cut is accented with a slim pony tail,
it hangs like a limp rope from his occiput.
She flounces her mini-skirt like a sailboat's sail,
leans on his tatooed arm, isn't she cute?
These fugitives are from a High School class,
they glance at the senior citizens, who are older.
In each hand, they hold a smoking stick of grass,
tank tops cling tenaciously to their shoulders.
But when the next metro rail train stops,
the kids thumb their noses at the ticket machine.
They head toward two vacant seats and flop,
pull out two fresh burger's, crisp and lean.
Meanwhile the old folks search, finally find a seat,
inspect fellow passengers before settling in.
They glance around the car, clean and neat,
and watch the kids throw trash, paper, tin.

The elder seniors look around for a sign,
for they have sandwiches in their paper bag.
"No eating," a lady said, "it's a $250 fine!"
"No smoking either," the kids take a drag.
The picnic lunch is put away real fast,
but the younger ones continue to chaw and munch.
When a deputy sheriff comes along at last,
the teenagers have already finished their lunch.
Litter and trash are scattered around their knees,
the white heads still remain hungry as bears.

The fast train soars above freeways, palms and trees,
at station stops, people come and go in ones and pairs.
Babies in strollers, mothers with children chains,
students with backpacks also drift on in.
Graffiti walls, abandoned factories, old trains,
whiz by its windows along with flop houses, gardens of sin.
The wrinkled faces of the aged ones
gape in wonder at youth's rebellion.
Young take chances, they think it's fun,
to act foolish, turn into devilish hellions.
Old folks play it safe, abide by the rules,
experience has taught them how to behave.
Young smart alecks, they really are the fools,
they flirt and dance around an early grave.

Like broken soap bubbles floating in the air,
the high school seniors suddenly disappear.
A ticket taker, spot checking to confirm the fare,
glance at the old couple's which they make appear.
Safe in the security of the blue line laws,
those senior citizens speed toward the city.
Flagrant youth, defying even their moms and paws,
have jumped from the moving train, O what a pity!

ADAM

His father pulled him out of the dust and dirt,
and made him into a man sudden-like.
The two never went on a Boy Scout hike
nor did his father teach him how to ride a bike.
No one showed him how to fly his kite,
shoot marbles, nor climb upon a pony's back.
His father never yelled at Little League games,
nor played rough and tumble on the floor.
His Dad never took him packpacking
nor walking to the duck pond in the park.

This father missed baby-burping him,
didn't take videos of learning how to swim.
No one taught him how to laugh and sing,
how to pick berries and many other things.
No pop took him hunting or fishing,
nor taught him reading, writing or wishing.
His father didn't shoot baskets with him,
didn't show him how to shuffle cards,
carve wood, whistle or make bird calls.

His father never took him to work
nor showed him how to handle Daddy's quirks.
He never took him to a city fountain,
to Disneyland nor Magic Mountain.
This poor lad missed Cub Scout Derbies,
go-cart races and Halloween's funny faces.
His Dad didn't even go to his graduation
nor did he fret over Eve's infaturation.

Maybe if together they had done some of these,
Cain and Abel would have been more at ease.

JB-97

90

ODE TO JIM'S WIFE*

Jim flipped through a stack of cards,
and came up with the Queen of Hearts.
He admired her symmetrical sweetness,
in her royal robe and fancy jacket.

Only his glasses could have seen such style,
so Muriel became Jim's Queen of Hearts.
Sweeping his love off to Las Vegas,
she glimmered like a star with her glamour.

As a grandmother, sipping tea,
her goodness ever seemed to increase.
Never doomed to be an old maid at all,
she became Jim's wife forever more.

*From a critique of the print, Queen of Hearts.

Spring, 1997 by the   Printmaking Class.

91

BALLAD OF BOB JUDSON

It was Bob Judson who got the blame,
with his open countenance, thinning white hair,
he's not the crime type. With his good name,
a ready smile and twinkling eyes, he was square.
All the neighbors knew this friendly man,
he shared corn and beans from his big garden.
He grew tomatoes, potatoes for the frying pan,
rabbits, woodchucks were the only ones he banned.
When gophers tore up the yards and lawns,
he went to his trusty twenty-two,
where with a marksman's eye and lazy yawn,
those pesky pests were promptly subdued.

When the Smith's horses kept escaping
from flimsy fences and rotten stalls,
Bob was sent to help with their landscaping
and an electric fence was soon installed.
When the Anderson's pool sprung a leak,
everyone expected Bob to stop the flood.
He diverted the water into a nearby creek,
and patched the bottom with thick sticky mud.
A retired farmer, Bob road his tractor mower,
around his three acres on the city fringes,
where his green thumb made him a plant grower,
he kept wood paths open and repaired gate hinges.

When Mr. Roberts, two doors down,
brought home his shepherd guard dog,
the neighbors became frightened all around
and no one would go for a walk or jog.
It broke out of its pen, chased Mrs. Albright,
and tore the Daniel's daschund all to shreds.
Bob was delegated to set things right,
so he went over there and found the Roberts in bed.
He spoke to them in a very nice way,
the dog left Bob alone as he was unafraid.
Two days later, the dog again broke away,
and killed the Thomas' cat, white and grayed.
Then when Bob asked them to contain it,
"There's no problem," is what Roberts said.
"Please keep it home," said Bob, "or train it!"
The beast was again put back into its shed.

At 2 am, Alfred Miller heard a ruckus out back,
where the chickens in his coop were squawking.
He quickly grabbed his shotgun from its rack,
saw a dark form come out running, not walking.
Two loud blasts split the still night air,
and the low streaking shadow fell dead.
The next morning, Bob was called
to carry the dead shepherd to Roberts' shed.
No one in the neighborhood cried or bawled,
but the Roberts fumed, mad as an old wet hen.
Now they don't speak to Bob anywhere,
but children play and mothers walk again.
So rabbits, gophers, woodchucks, beware!

SHIRLEY TEMPLE'S SHOES

There they were, in a glass case
in the Museum's treasure room.
Their gleaming patent leather black
reflected a soft light.
They rested there, looking
as if she had just stepped
out of them yesterday,
though sixty years have passed.
Both buckled straps lay
across polished arch tops,
casting dark straight shadows
over smooth white insides.
Black heels and leather soles
ran toward the rounded toes,
where creased ripple folds
turned them up slightly.

When I saw that discarded pair
of tiny well kept shoes,
I remembered that
when we both were six,
I had decided to marry her.

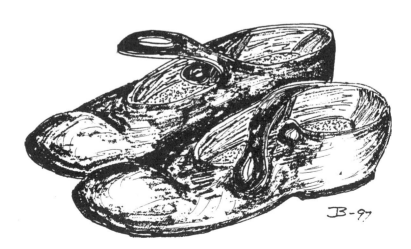

B-97

94

While Shirley in frilly dresses
and golden curls, tapped
her way to fame,
I ran shirtless and barefooted
down a cow pasture lane.
In those Depression days,
her studio removed the metal taps
from those shoes to use
on her new larger pair.
In those summer boyhood days,
my mother removed our shoes,
to save their soles and heels,
until school started in the fall.
We listened to the clackity clack
of those famous shoes on our radio,
but Shirley never heard the soft thud
of our calloused feet
tromping on the bare wooden floor.

MY DOG COOKIE

Cookie barks at me
and wants to play squeaky ball.
I'm not a stranger
like the washer repair man,
so she barks but does not bite.

BOOKS ON SHELVES

Books rest on the shelves,
only covers have been read.
I want to explore
their inner facts and knowledge,
if I should live long enough.

MORA THE MERMAID

Mora the Mermaid calls from her rock,
No lighthouse sends out its beaming light,
My days are few, I hear death knock.

I walk alone upon the wooden dock,
Those strolling by don't know my plight,
Mora the Mermaid calls from her rock.

My shirt is tattered, a hole is in my sock,
I eat from dumpsters, then run all night,
My days are few, I hear death knock.

I've traveled years and city blocks,
Stopping at missions that preach the right,
While Mora the Mermaid calls from the rocks.

Stinking and smelling like I have the pox,
I stumble along the streets and alley sites,
My days are few, death now knocks.

Homeless, I'm just a dark and shapeless sight,
When I'm gone, others will replace my blight.
Mora the Mermaid calls from her rock,
My days are few, I hear death knock.

FOR JOHN

A little gray Porsche scoots by,
    across the Gerald Desmond bridge,
just as the early morning sun climbs
    over the top of Saddleback Mountain.
A fair haired Latvian, called "Janis"
    is hunched inside, hiding
an internal iron will, which finally
    even made the Russians give up.
Like a bumper car at Magic Mountain,
    the low riding Porsche
bounces from hospital to hospital
    from early morning to late night.

The man seated in this small machine,
    carries patience with him,
built upon long renal access hours
    or urgency powered by burst aortas.
Unknown to many, he packs and sends
    surplus unwanted drugs, dressings,
instruments of healing, concern,
    to fellow East European countrymen.
To the lame and the legless,
    his pleasant manner inspires them,
or those with clogged carotids,
    his optimism encourages hope.

He teaches residents his art,
    shares his thoughts and ideas,
instructs nurses in the best way,
    then shows them how.
In committees and at meetings,
    he sets high performance standards,
and challenges his surgical peers
    to practice the best they can.
Now another decade has passed by,
    John still buzzes around our town.
May his little gray Porsche car
    continue to streak across the sky.

IT HAPPENS

One summer morning when I was only four,
while out picking black berries with my Dad,
I had to go number two, real bad,
but somehow could not do it there.

Uncle Ray was lodged in the outhouse out back
with its buzzing flies and its Sears catalogue.
A neighbor lady was gossiping with mother,
to and fro on the rustic wooden porch swing.

The unpainted, battered porch steps were askew,
my baby sister was trapped in her white playpen.
Toys were scattered around the peeling paint floor,
so I dropped my pants and laid a turd gently there.

Brother Ben yelled, screamed and pointed
to the brown excrement lying peacefully serene.
Mother leaped into action with crimson face,
and turned my bare bottom a stinging red.

Animals can leave scat along their trails,
and night soil is used in wet rice paddies.
That day I learned little boys cannot dump,
like a dog, on Uncle Ray's gray front porch.

JERRY

Like a white tailed deer, he ran
through our years too fast.
Please remember, if you can,
Jerry Church's life from the past.

Superior water below fifty for him,
(his thermometer wouldn't lie)
meant skipping his morning swim,
(and he returned home with a sigh.)

He explored the northern woods,
knew the name of all the birds.
He went about doing good,
cared for others with kind words.

He loved his large family,
helped Joanne care for all the kids.
Jerry read books voraciously,
until his health hit the skids.

Each sunrise, each sunset,
these were his special times.
He lived his life without regret,
learned Creation's rhythms, its rhymes.

He always had a ready smile,
especially for those down cast.
Jerry always walked that second mile,
lifted spirits, healed the sick unasked.

So, I pause to give him my final tribute,
a friend, a fellow physician, a fine man.
A weeping willow has been planted to salute
Jerry's return to Lake Superior's sand.

ROY

Nuisance chipmunks didn't have a chance,
    "papa's box" caught them as they danced.
Transported to some far off wood,
    they scrambled free as they should.

Tiny hummingbirds flitted around,
    sucking sweet fluid without a sound.
Red breasted grosbeaks, cardinals, finches,
    cracked seeds to meet their needs
    and added color to bare porch benches.

Fish swam around his pontoon boat,
    they were caught by "pill-pill" floats.
Maples and pines were thinned out,
    his new house was built strong and stout.

The lake changed with each passing season,
    Roy kept his smile and his reason.
His family was his most precious wealth,
    you soon forgot his limp, his failing health.

Talking, laughing, the joke's on us,
    until the end, he remained curious.
It is hard to put into words all his gags,
    he now has left his birds, the little wags.

Temporary quarters have been exchanged
    for a permanent home upon the range.
Far from his R-V trailer tall,
    he roams beyond our loudest call.

Though Roy has gone to some unknown place,
    we'll never forget his smiling face.
A weeping willow has been planted near,
    to remember Roy Schmidt whom we loved dear.

JANUS

According to ancient Roman mythology,
Janus was the god, if you please,
of beginnings and endings.
Two faced, he sat upon his throne
to open gates with his keys,
closing, locking them when finished.
His two countenances did not imply
duplicity, only vigilance.
One is youth, always looking ahead,
the other that of an old man
peering into the past tense.
His right hand held a sceptre
by which he controlled man,
his ups and downs, his fortune,
his work, his art, his religion.
The Romans only closed the gates
to his temple in times of peace.
(In 700 years of Roman rule,
they were closed only three times.)
The term "janitor", keeper of the keys,
came from his name as did the first month.
His festive day was celebrated
on the first day of each new year.

Now as we watch the old year leave again,
our one great Creator God,
points us toward a new one ahead.
It is He who holds the air, the sea,
the land, in the hollow of His hand.
Like Janus of those ages long ago,
God controls the gates of Heaven.
He is the spirit of our new beginnings,
the breath of our life renewed.

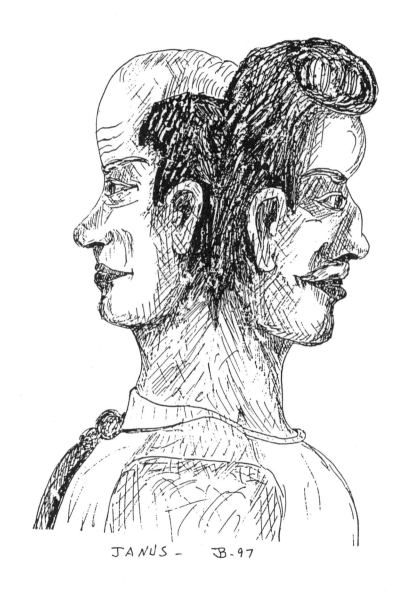

JANUS - B-97

MATTHEW

Matthew retired from his medical practice
and helped in our animal research lab.
His classic handle bar moustache
was noticed first where ever he went.
(We never could get him
to wear a surgical mask.)
It stuck to his round wrinkled face
like a Hollywood disguise.
Perched above his thin mouth,
he kept it waxed and twirled
so it stood straight out
to underline the two twinkling
gray piercing eyes.
A white goatee on a receding chin
pointed downward to a rope plaited tie
with its slide of a giant "M"
slung around his neck.
His hair was thin in front,
uncut out back
and showed the ravages
of his 72 years of living.
Once over six feet tall,
his drooping shoulders
and baggy over-washed jeans
told of his crumbling
physical stature.
The bottoms of the jeans
were tucked into cowboy boots,
scuffed, worn and unpolished.
A dull plaid shirt
matched the red bandana
tied loosely around his throat.
A felt, ten gallon hat
was hung from the chin rope
down is hump curved back.

Matthew always had many questions,
inquiring about everything he saw,
just like a kid at the zoo.

With a PhD in radiology,
pathology and medicine at least,
he felt qualified to serve
as a helper in the surgical
dog research laboratory.
He had a way with animals,
coaxing dogs to silence
as he cleaned and scrubbed
their cages each day.

He drove a 1957 Cadillac "boat"
that suffered three flats
one day when he drove
into the parking lot
over the outgoing spikes.
His curiosity and intelligent
questions challenged
the researchers, kept them
honest and true also.
He dressed in the green
surgical scrub suits,
but always wore his large
Texas hat to keep the O.R.
light out of his eyes.
Gentle with the animals,
he became friends with each,
and grieved when one
did not survive the experiment.

Matthew began to falter
and stumble about the lab,
so one day he appeared
with a fancy gentleman's cane.
A year or two passed
with him helping
and handling the animals.
One day, he had a big stroke
so we put his tools away.
We missed his moustache,
it was never seen there again.
Matthew is gone now,
and the dogs don't bark the same.

J3-98

106

KAY K.'S STUFFED DOG

For many years it sat
on the top shelf of my locker
in the hospital operating room.
A circular mirror perched
on its cloth brow, reflected
light. A black wire stethoscope
was draped around seamed shoulders.
Fuzzy yellow ears hung down
on either side of a red nose.
Tufts of orange felt hair
sprouted from the round top
of a slightly cocked head.

This queer little creature
was Kay K.'s, head nurse of Room 10,
an arena where in the early years,
open heart surgery battles were fought.
With flashing wit, she joked
and teased the surgeons
to help them "loosen up."
I was young, shy and a family man,
so she would embarrass me by
chasing me around the operating room,
threatening, "I'll kiss you, Doctor!"
I can still see her sputtering
and laughing when a couple
of surgeons dumped her into a bag
with the dirty linen.

Later Kay had received a needed pacemaker,
so in gratitude and also as a joke,
she gave me the little "doggy doctor."
It sat on my locker shelf for a long time,
watching as I changed into "scrubs"
or went charging off on hospital rounds.
One Friday afternoon, while taking off
for the weekend in their plane,
Kay and her husband suddenly went down.

Her stuffed dog now sits there on my empty desk,
and flashes its strange stitched smile.
Tear drop shapes, painted black and white,
are just its wistful eyes staring at me.

IMMIGRANTS SESTINA

A sense of real accomplishment may be achieved
if we analyze carefully every committed crime.
Whether these are done by illegal immigrants,
a safe cracker or only a petty thief,
such analysis will count. There is no substitute
for learning how to interpret the law.

When wrong doers flee from an officer of the law,
they won't stop running until freedom is achieved.
They feel it is better to die than to substitute
a sense of guilt or surrender for their crime.
More than one great criminal started as a thief,
before coming here as unwanted immigrants.

Even the Mafia began as Sicilian immigrants,
who upon arrival immediately flouted the law.
Trained and nurtured how to be a thief,
wealth, social status were soon achieved.
Families, children, all were taught crime,
the FBI found there seldom was a substitute.

Replacing new world morality with a substitute,
a different code of ethics came from these immigrants.
Some became involved in organized crime,
while others chose to be police or judges of the law.
All hoped some sense of reality would be achieved
before the mob wiped them out like a common thief.

For many it was a badge of honor to be a thief.
If you were honest and upright, a substitute
for the killing and shooting which the mob achieved,
you might be sacrificed with other legal immigrants.
Thus it became necessary to enact Federal law
to catch the racketeers in their hidden crime.

Most of these men engaged in white collar crime,
bank embezzlement or fraud, like a clever thief.
The Justice Department used the new law
to pursue and prosecute those who had tried to substitute
legal alternatives for their illegal immigrants
status. For many of these crooks, capture was achieved.

For other gangsters, however, it was not achieved
as prosecuters defined and outlined their crime.
This conflict effected the lives of legal immigrants
who are hard workers and not just some foreign thief.
These people are good citizens and do not substitute
immorality for goodwill and understanding of the law.'

So rather than substitute violence for the law,
we need to stop the thief and expose criminals in their crime.
Tolerance will then be achieved with acceptance of immigrants.

MUSETTE

My desk at the Nationale Bibliotheque
is piled high with books, papers, theses.
My research into French women painters
of the nineteenth and twenthieth centuries
is going ever so slowly, dragging really.
I really live in Canada, that is,
in the Maritime provinences
but I left my husband and three children
for six weeks to work here in Paris.
Right now, I'm at a chamber music concert
in Saint Chappelle, sitting
next to a noisy American on vacation here.
When the Vivaldi is over
I must get back to my books.

The colors of the stained glass windows
gleam like jewels from the evening sun,
and cast a spell over my tired mind.
Spring, summer, autumn, winter,
the four seasons slip by rapidly.
Oh, to be in Montreal again,
to be away from these simple people
who cannot appreciate French literature.
Quebec, where French is loved and reverred,
that's where my research tells me go.

A summer rain dampens the walks outside,
the applause breaks my reverie.
If I hurry, I can get in another 30 minutes
of study before the library closes
for the night. My legs carry me out
of this ancient king's chapel.
Women painters and poets, I salute you!

AUBADE

I rise before the sun comes up,
bouncing out of our bed,
the dog barks and wakes
up your sleeping form.
I run and sport upon the hill,
you read the morning _Times_.
Then whiskers fall,
sweat is showered away,
you wander around the house
in faded blue chemise.
Breakfast boxes sprout
upon the barren table,
daily pills are pitched
down each gullet hatch.
Bright oranges match
your glowing rosy cheeks,
fresh milk polishes
your gorgeous ivory smile.
I put my books in my bag,
then struggle out the door.
When I kiss you
"so-long" each day,
I may travel far and wide,
but your loving face
and your happy smile,
accompany me all the while.

MURIEL

What I need is you
to walk with me along the river path,
to sit down with me upon its grassy bank
and watch the wood ducks float by.
What I need is you to see
with me, the birch tree change its bark,
from a glossy black to a mature matte white.
I need you to poke the giant bullfrog's behind,
sitting there immovable upon the lawn,
and watch the green monster jump a foot or two.
I think of you as the tiny ducklings
scurry and huddle around their mother,
frightened by my heavy step upon the grass.
What I need is a companion
to stroll with me among these ancient oaks,
whose fresh green leaves give life
to the ponderous massive trunks.
I need someone else's eyes
to see the veil of mist lifting from the swamp,
to watch the spiked sun rise above the trees.
I need your nose to smell the wild roses,
your touch to heal my wounded heart.
I need to know what it means
that after forty-five years together,
you are no longer at my side.
I need you to tell me what kind
of bird this is, perched upon the fence,
its yellow head and golden breast,
trying with song to bring joy
to my empty and tortured mind.
Stand with me beneath this weeping willow,
wipe away the tears falling upon your grave.
What I need is you, my departed wife.

POEMS FROM AN INNER PLACE

YELLOW LILY ON THE HILLSIDE

Yellow lily, growing on the hillside,
you reach out towards my hand
as if I were your only sun.
Your golden petaled face
invites me to plunge into your bosom
like a darting hummingbird.
Your slim and tender leaves
rustle and dance before me
as if I were the blowing breeze.
Your roots suck and nourish
the slender stalk bent my way
as if I were Mother Earth.

Yet, it is I who want to taste
your sweet honeyed nectar
like the bees buzzing in your place.
It is I who must look and see
the moon glow of your soft petals
as they shimmer in the morning sun.
It is I that must root out weeds,
that choke out a growing life,
as the gardener's hoe has done.
Only then can I reach out to you
and touch your truth and beauty,
yellow lily blooming on the hillside.

THE BOSS

Alluding to a poem "The Pulley" by George Herbert (1633)

When She first made man
She had her department store full of goods.
She said, "I'll give him all I can,
all the world's gifts and presents.
They are thrown about everywhere
so I'll gather them together for his pleasure.

At the gym, this man became muscular and strong,
while the barber/hairdresser made him handsome.
Professors gave him wisdom and knowledge.
When the gifts were nearly gone,
She said, "Stop! There rests one more
back at the warehouse I would spare.

If I give this man My final hidden jewel,
he will adore My gifts and forget Me.
Mother Nature and Myself will be losers
in Our great experiment with this creature
who rules the laws which We have made.

Man can have everything except the rest;
it all will make him rich but weary.
If he does what's right, honors justice,
loves his fellow man while he looks for Me,
then when I call, he will throw away it all.

JB-96

Ganesa Dancing

117

STOP SIGN

I stand alone at my corner,
feet anchored in concrete,
staid and stoic, rigid,
my red head is unmoved.
Motorists glance at my face,
barely see the message there,
written in white block letters
they learned in kindergarten.
A cardboard garage sale sign
is strapped across my chest,
dogs lift their legs on mine.
My sister, living a block away,
is strapped to a lamp post,
her crimson blush defiled
by black spray paint graffiti.
A brother hides in Washington, D.C.
surrounded by highway signs,
one way arrows, street names,
no parking notices, numbers.

Life rushes by each day,
no one slows or cares.
I watch in metal horror
as a reckless driver ignores me
and runs over a tiny child.
An old lady trundles across the walk
and speeding low riders
dare my pleading voice.
Exhaust fumes corrode my lungs,
birds dump on my forehead.
A drunk rams my midsection
and curves my metal spine.
I wave my only message
through rain, fog or deepest night.
Everyone seems out of tune,
they do not hear my song.
Someday, they will also know
that what I have to say
means they all must obey.

CROWS

My father was a gentle man,
he loved earth's various creatures.
However, he always disparagingly said,
"Two pests must go, rats and crows!"

I know they raided his newly planted corn,
they ate seeds and tender plants.
His vegetable garden suffered loss
in spite of his planted scarecrow tree.

In flocks of two or twenty,
they caw and squawk mockingly.
They rob other nests of eggs and young,
they feast upon garbage at the dump.

Crows hover over landfills, fresh road kills,
they eat other repulsive refuse too.
They seem to crave everything or anything,
good or bad, alive or dead, old or new.

Early in the morning, they raise their cry,
then is when they raise the loudest ruckus.
Decibels flee from the city park trees,
sidewalks turn white below their roosts.

Shy around man, they run like demons,
flapping and flopping their awkward wings.
It is hard to think of any good they do,
if they were gone, I wouldn't even miss 'em!

119

A DEAD FISH

Crows loudly croak and squawk
along the grassy river bank,
out beyond where the path
takes a sharp right angled turn.
They flap and strut on the rocky river ledge
above a discarded Minute Maid can,
held fast at the dry high water mark,
perched next to a trapped charred log.

On the grassy bluff
among the white clover stems,
between puffed dandelion balls
and tiny yellow sand burr flowers,
lies a huge dead fish.
Nearly two feet long, fat and succulent,
it could have fallen out of a polaroid photo.
Its eye sockets are both picked clean
by the voracious crows.
Its small mouth with rigid jaws
is turned inside out, puckered open,
while flies swarm upon its useless gills.

From a foamy head, brown black scales,
rises a strong fishy stench.
Its yellow belly gleams in the sultry sun,
still tail and fins are motionless.
Unable to swim in the humid air
or flip its tail to navigate the grass,
it lies there where it perished.
So close to its murky river home,
stretched out along its vital source,
it now lays rotting
on the nearby shore.

Dead bass, how often my spirit seems to die,
when I flounder upon the cay,
unable to breathe life's essence there.
I am old, my belly also turns yellow
and my crusted scales are thick.
Crows pluck at my blind eyes,
worms consume my wasting flesh,
whenever I leave the river
and climb up through its mud.

Rank fish upon the embankment,
whose soul has fled away,
know that I too will soon be dead.
As my body rots and bones decay,
may my spirit fly away with yours.

The sign says "No Parking Here"
so I must continue to stroll along.
I pass the rusty manhole cover
that reads "Neehah Foundry Co.
        Neehah, Wis."
Slow down, don't walk so fast,
"Speed Limit 35."
I march past four mailboxes
in a row, 1 white - 3 black.
The brilliant red fire hydrant
stands alone in the center
of the grassy boulevard
where the steel guard rail
is strapped to wooden posts
with rounded bolts, square nuts.
A rusty chain, slung from pole to pole,
keeps me out of the river
and the burdock burrs too.
A broken brown beer bottle
and a clear plastic "Pancheros"
drinking cup lie upon the ground
beneath a spider web
in which a dragon fly is trapped.

I am shriveled up like closed bells
of those morning glories
waiting for the dawn.
I wait for my lavender petals to bloom,
to give the world my truth
when my walk is done.

ONE WORD POEMS

Mark
cries
but
Grandma
is
there.

No
smoking
eating
drinking
skateboards
bicycles
roller-blades
graffiti
sex.

Cambus
stops,
doors
fly
open.
She
alights,
he
steps
up
and
in.

The
book
falls
open
to
a
poem
about
love
and
death.

The
old
concrete
bench
clearly
says
L.A.
Class
of
1914.

THE CAMPER TRUCK

Curbside at dawn,
          on Toscanini hill,
is parked an old camper,
          stoically still.

Its license plate is black
          with yellow bands,
all caked, splattered with mud
          and desert sands.

Four corroded aluminum
          lawn chairs
are roped across its rear
          door in pairs.

Weather beaten pieces
          of old cardboard
cover its top and a
          jammed dashboard.

The front seat is
          packed with junk,
ribbons from horse, dog shows,
          brown paper chunks.

Old newspapers, Kleenix boxes,
          dirty sox, T-shirts,
running shoes, gloves, coke cans,
          mix with worn out skirts.

What clutter collector
          owns this outfit?
There's hardly room
          for the driver to sit!

ROOM 145, A DAYSINN NIGHT

The cold North Carolina wind chills the bones,
street lights glare with their yellow halos.
Construction workers are at their homes,
or at Charlotte's bars with other tired fellows.

An elderly couple creeps across the asphalt,
fingering their electronic motel door keys.
A gust of the arctic north makes them halt,
at room one forty five where they seize

the plastic card key with its black band.
Thrusting it deep into the metal slot,
no green light illuminates the hand,
the door stayed locked, thus was their lot.

Pulling out the card, peering into its face,
shivers ran through both wrinkled skins.
More attempts were made to get in their place,
but nothing worked to let them enter in.

Peeking through the window, they saw their stuff,
on the other side of the anti-theft barrier.
A trip to the office was not enough
as the master card key did not work either.

Phone calls, running trips across the parking lot,
revealed an emergency key was hours away.
Another room was opened, that's what they got.
Thawing while sleeping in banquet clothes ended their day.

It was at six am, before the morning's glow,
the manager woke them from their slumber.
"Your room is open, sorry to inconvenience you so."
Room one forty five, they'll remember that number.

J3-97

Printmaking Critiques

1. Mike's Monoprint

While I sit in my prison cell alone,
a big, long rainbow appears in the window.
My thoughts are chopped and epic,
the bold connecting colors are abstract.
My contemporary feelings are expressionistic,
like a child doing a finger painting.
The cinematic, primary rainbow
still floods my huge dungeon darkness.
I am furious that I cannot reach out
like a macho man or a god,
to grasp Mike's monoprint and place it
upon my own artistic page.

2. Jeff's Stencil

The white pavement stretches over wheat fields,
an endless highway of Route 66,
rolls over my field of dreams.
I head west on a Greyhound bus,
and the country speaks of mice and men,
of a middle America of clean surrealism.
The desert road disorients me for a moment,
like a Van Gogh quilt seen from the air,
with its crisp, simple patterns of green and gold.
A blue cloudless sky with white ribbon of Route 66,
roll on forever and take be back to the summer of "63.

3. Eric's Stencil

Bubble up, O' musical melody,
wrap your whimsical harmonic sounds
around my own strange universe of silence.
O' how your fertile lyrical notes
strum upon my intestinal feelings,
like some accomplished flowing song.
Your spontaneous rhythms flow like fluid,
among the simple calligraphic images
that linger in my sandy mind.
Bubble on O' spiral shapes, space like
in your own strange universe,
sprinkle down your truth for me to see.

HOUSING DEVELOPMENT

At the Horizon Cooperative Homes,
an old dominant male is screaming
at the ladies and passive immature males.
The ruckus splits the early morning air
like a woodsman's axe on firewood.
Circling and tugging like young kids
at the playground, each poke and probe
for holes in the argument.
Blooming morning glories are open
but turn away in shame.
Crows yap and gawk, first encourage
one side and then the other in the dispute.
In pure white suits they circle around,
old gray beard not conceding an inch.
The screeching sea gulls fight
over a piece of dumpster garbage.

127

MIRROR

I rest, round or square
upon the wall or cabinet.
I stand, long or short,
cling to the bedroom door.
Those who peer into my face,
see themselves as I do.

Mist clouds my shiney glass,
steam rises from the shower.
Whiskers drop off,
a shaver hums its tune.
Lipstick pops from the tube,
marches across the mouth.
As she preens and coos,
herself I have become.

I present another fantasy room,
yet in it lies the true.
As the years roll by,
the masks change within.
In me, one can see himself,
I return what I've perceived.

Look into my window,
see my predicament.
I can only tell honest truth,
I only speak to what I know.
I reveal to those who see,
what is, not what's to be.

LEG MEN, REJOICE!
(Your Time Has Come)

Spring fashion uncovers legs that talk,
shorts expose those bare lower limbs.
Cloned shapely gams parade the walks,
knees are out (or should I say are in?)
I gaze and look with art appreciation,
"Pervert! Pervert!" some one yells at me.
My tantrums of winter's deprivation
are worse than a smoker's without a stogie.

Arturo Fuente double coronas look fatter
than thunder thighs above cigar shaped calves.
Even bioethics is no laughing matter
with such legs pumping like precision valves.
Fat legs come early or late in life's innings,
without any exercise, they grow big over night.
So a make over of female underpinnings
happens when liposuction supplants cellulite.

Entrepeneurs, there is no market ban,
for a product that still stands tall.
Women's legs aren't coerced by any plan
unless it seems to careem off the wall.
Customers rebel against small ankle tatoos
while bikini makers promote trim designs.
Beach tanning replaces the salon taboos,
women won't acknowledge their sagging lines.

Men, exchange photographs, now in vogue,
your love of legs still makes you sigh.
So stare with popping eyes, you rogue,
breathe in fast and adore those thighs.

129

ICE CREAM TRUCK

Hear
the tinkle song,
comes the ice cream man.

Tingle,
tingle, like a broken record,
it plays on and on.

Smell
spring or summer,
that's when he comes.

See
red and yellow, blue
balloons painted on the white.

Run
to get the children
coins, stopped in their play.

Empty
all the yards
and neighbor houses too.

Gather
all the little chicks
around the mother hen.

Stop
your moving cars,
let the fat lady sing.

Watch
cones and ice cream bars
appear as if by magic.

Taste
the sweet chocolate,
vanilla of smooth winter.

Toot
your horn,
pied piper plays his tune.

CHRISTMAS POEM

Send
season's cards,
good, grateful, prayerful.
Asking, seeking, giving, loving,
new, old, traditional
faces, places
spend.

Turns
memories, hands
glad, folded, sad.
Touching, greeting, meeting, laughing.
Green tinseled Yule
fireplace, log
burns.

Ring
bells, sleighs.
Jolly, happy, white,
Ringing, glistening, shining, remembering.
Red, shiney silver,
trees, holidays
sing.

I SIT IN THE LIBRARY

Where my blue book bag lies crumpled
    upon the dusty desk.
Where the bulletin board is papered
    with best selling book covers.
Where a girl's purse has brown
    leather straps wound around its body.
Where a dark wooden chair resides
    with its soft inviting seat.
Where green computer screens name
    wanted and unwanted authors, themes.
Where scholars are often hard at work,
    while the water fountains won't.
Where a sign is posted on a concrete pillar
    that says "No eating, No drinking."
Where a stiff book cover has springs
    ready to snap shut on its knowledge.
Where the clock hands move
    either fast or slow, that depends.
Where an arrow points to room 225W
    an inner sanctum of mystery, intrigue.
Where row upon row of weaving shelves
    thread thousands of unread books.
Where striped furrows of the carpet
    run to a vanishing point beyond the window.
Where the tiled steps climb up and in
    or lead me down and out.

ARS POETICA

A poem should not have to speak or talk,
nor should it ever have to take a walk.
Its words can shower down like the rain,
sprouting new thoughts from a dusty brain.
New ideas may blossom like a flower,
poetry draws upon some hidden power.
Is a poem meant to converse with me,
carry me far across some distant sea?
Will singing songs from its hidden words
convey truth to galloping human herds?
Staggered lines can carry meaning too,
revealing to diggers what may be true.
A poem lives its own solitary life,
bringing happiness, joy or strife.
It tells of the sun or perhaps the moon,
makes me laugh, cry or swoon.
A poem cannot be made or crafted,
it cannot be spoken, written or drafted.
Because it grows upon a slender stalk,
it is, remains, even without any talk.

A SONNET SIXTY FIVE

When I was young, I went to many schools,
my teachers were all so old.
They filled the brains of other fools
and poured gold into my own mind mold.
They gave me wisdom, good advice,
guided me how to search and grope.
Parents taught me to be polite and nice,
read, learn and always have hope.
Now I'm old and go to school again,
my teachers are now so young.
They stretch ideas to fit my rigid pen,
make new songs which I've never sung.
Young professors force me to forget my past,
look to the future for as long as I can last.

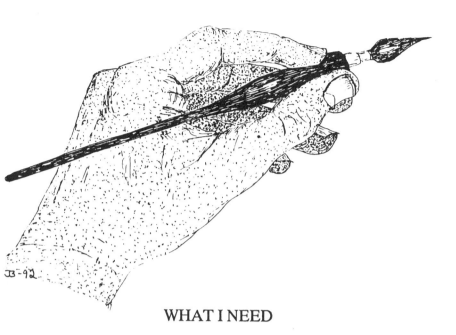

WHAT I NEED

What I need is time to lift my pen
and run it across a writing pad.
What I need is new vision to sprout
in the vacant soil of my brain,
to burst forth as a blooming insight.
Language roots need
to sink deep into my muscles,
take nourishment and make ideas grow.
What I need is the ink to run
from my finger tips, running pen,
with coursing blood carrying
my all from skull to extremity.
Also what I need is a gardener,
to prune away excess verbiage,
trim away useless phrases, branches
flying off in all directions.
What I need is some new nurture
for the growth potential of my stem.
Fresh water and enlightenment
need to fall upon my leaves
to bring forth any truth
or beauty hiding there.

MT. PISGAH CEMETERY

On Mount Pisgah Church Road, all alone,
there lies an old cleared farmer's field.
Rows of granite stones have grown
above the tombs which earth has sealed.
Family pillars of rock, Davis, Johnson, Yates,
are standing stiff like silent guards,
hovering over their relations and mates.
Their houses are vacant, empty are the yards,
feuds, family fights have been settled long ago
as they all sleep together far below.

Surrounding one ancient burial plot
is an black iron fence with its small gate.
Is it there to keep the living out
or trap those within who are of late?
A solitary tree grants them shade
from the hot North Carolina sun.
Clumps of bright plastic flowers fade
where they are clamped to granite buns.
Are these tokens for those who pass this way,
or for the dead who have passed away?

I wander quietly in that headstone place,
looking for my name and for my dates.
Who will trim the grass from around my space,
put flowers on my grave and on my mates?
Just when will my life leave its nest,
and where will my small spot of soil be?
Who knows where my bones will rest,
where is my own Mt. Pisgah cemetery?

THE SNACK CART

A red and white umbrella tilts,
casting shade over a
University hot dog stand.
My stomach growls over weiner smells
and I laugh at bags of potato chips
and pretzel snacks hanging
there by their ears.
Muffins are stacked

in a basket, waiting.
Bottles of orange and purple pop stand
above glass covered shelves
filled with soft twisted pretzels.
Like dancers in performance, loops
of browned flour with salt burrs,
pose in perfect oval formations.

A black haired lady with pink glasses,
sorts out the bananas and apples.
She dumps ice upon the coke cans,
putters around her defined space,
and pokes at all her food paraphernalia.

She hands a pretzel to blue denim slacks
with white T-shirt and black Sierra backpack.
A brown wallet floats above the counter
and greenbacks snap into the cash register.
A white styrofoam cup spills over its creamed coffee
and then leaves clutched in a professor's hand.

Weather beaten canvas with scalloped fringes
hangs from rusted awning poles
and discarded boxes lie beneath a table.
A late afternoon sun sends shafts
of spring light through blooming trees

and students dwindle away, business dies.
The cart folds up its warming trays,
tucks away its napkins, catsup,
even the mustard jar disappears.

I suddenly feel alone as soft rubber wheels
roll silently away. The empty snack cart
lumbers off to join its clones,
to roost like birds for the night.

Only a vacant tent remains.

MAKE THE BEST OF IT

Gather flowers while you're able,
eat your meals while at the table.
Read all the best books you can,
plant your garden with a steady hand.

See stars in the clearest night,
use your eyes while you've sight.
Listen to the classics, learn the music,
hear laughter as you perform your tricks.

Play games of youth with their balls,
run or walk, before you fall.
Eat healthy foods, save your change,
learn the unknown, know the strange.

The beginning is made for the end,
the middle is the best, my friend.
So do not fear what's in between,
work for the best in any scheme.

SUNRISE

Sailing ships float across the eastern sky
the purple night still trapped
in their billowing, rolling forms.
Slivers of red slash across their hulls,
wakes of orange churn and glow
in oceans of misty atmosphere.
A robin trills its early morning song,
throws its bright breast against the dawn
daring the sky to match its rusty chest.
The jagged earth's edge is dark,
a saw cutting a picture piece
from changing chameleon clouds.
Pink birch bark trunks dance in the wood,
while a solitary white pine is silhouetted
dark against a cadmium yellow horizon.
Shifting pillows on the heavenly bed
turn orange, purple and deep red
as those sailing barks drift aimlessly by.

With a sudden explosion of energy
the life giving ball of sun appears
and turns the scattering fleet all white.
Like millions of years before today,
at exactly six forty one a.m.,
mother nature's repeat spectacle,
captures and holds my own transitory heart.

LICENTIOUS

Up, Licentious, up, I say. Stand straight
as a Marine on guard at the White House gate.
Salute those bosom buddies, those breasts,
that once adorned your rugged chest.
Raise your head and gaze out west,
before sleeping away your final rest.

Lazy soldier, indolent private, if you please,
why do you lie there so relaxed at ease?
There are forts to conquer, walls to breach,
rise at this Captain's unspoken speech.
Sing like the birds, fly upward now,
march to victory, let all before you bow.

Age may be either too old or young,
but you know when a love song's been sung.
Why not dance at the county fair,
part company with these old gray hairs.
Plunge ahead with unknown cares,
forage for pleasure in a bed of pears.

Tell me, you witless spaghetti lost,
why you no longer stand stiff at post?
Don't you guard man and his host,
won't you salute the general's ghost?
Do you only think of cultured arts
and not of man's many other parts?

Love has spoken to you in the past,
now you are slack in converse at last.
Fill your body with the sweetest repast,
lift your voice and sing mighty fast.
I need you now, you must obey,
don't desert me. Up, Licentious, up, I say.

JURY DUTY

The county courthouse stands there astute,
twelve stories high in the winter sun.
Its dark shadow falls quiet, mute,
across MLK Jr.'s memorial, the fallen one.
Entrance doors are guarded all around,
by gunned deputies and metal detectors.
They pop and hum with a warning sound,
as criminals walk through the protectors.
Elevators are crowded with crowds,
gangs and gals, lawyers in suits and ties.
Each is filled with brief cases, voices loud,
record boxes, summons, subpoenas and lies.
"Second floor! Cafeteria, traffic court,
and jury assembly room," someone says.
There, hundreds of people of every sort
lounge on sofa chairs, green or grays.
A few are at tables with puzzles askew,
others sleep or doze, stare or come and go.
A patriotic Pepsi machine watches too,
while some read books, knit or sew.
A lone window in the corner of the room
summons jurors to check in and then wait.
A loud speaker says go to lunch at noon,
take a break or go home until tomorrow late.
Citizens come here from all walks of life,
wondering who next will be called out loud.
Husbands are on the phone, calling the wife,
while the restless walk among the crowd.
Men, women, blacks, Asians, Hispanics too,
sit with workers, retirees, sick or well.
Housewives, students, doctors, lawyers few,
are dutifully imprisoned in this jury cell.
Newspapers are scattered about the place,
lunches or lap tops may pop out of bags.
Television blares a soap opera's steady pace,
panels are called just as waiting spirits sag.
Each person is ready to pass judgment
on society's evil, its injustice, wrongs.

Concentrated here for everyone's lament,
citizen jurors must listen to very sad songs.
It seems a waste of both money and time,
people's sensibilities and their thought.
Yet, how else can we cope with crime,
maintain law and order like we ought?
Though inefficient, consuming time anon,
the entire process seems out of control.
The jury system rumbles on and on,
plodding steadily toward a fairness goal.
In the courthouse standing there so tall,
juries seek equality and justice for all.

COMMENCEMENT FINALE

Hundreds of cars park in grassy field.
Thousands of parents, graduates sit in stadium.
Skies cloud over, president and speaker mount stand.
With first words of welcome, heavens open up.
Tons of water dump on faculty, friends, all graduates.
Degrees conferred in one minute.
Speech would be mailed.
Tasseled heads in ruined gowns,
families with soaked cameras,
wade into parking lot swamp.
Axel deep wheels sink into clay mud.
Shoes plucked off by muck.
Tow trucks quickly mired too.
Human chaos, confusion, frustration, despair.
Rain pours down for two hours.
Last car extracted well past midnight.

TALES FROM AROUND THE FIREPLACE

PHOEBE

Phoebe was the only girl in her class with such a name. In fact, Phoebe (pronounced Fee-bee) didn't know anyone else in the whole world with such a name. She knew Susans, Michelles, and Jennifers, but no Phoebes.

She had been named after Aunt Phoebe who had died the year before. Her Uncle Phillip now lived by himself on a farm in the country. Phoebe and her brother Phil went to their Uncle's farm for a visit when their parents had to take a trip. When the children went to the farm, they planned to stay for the whole summer. They explored the barn, ran in the pasture, hiked in the woods, milked the cows, fed the pigs and chickens. They played with Philemon the dog and Phineas the cat.

"Uncle Phillip," Phoebe called to her Uncle one day. "Come and see this nest these birds have built. They are working up under the milk shed eaves."

"Why, Phoebe, those birds have the same name as you do," he declared. He noticed the gray-brown pair wagging their long tails as they flitted about. "They are a member of the fly catcher family."

"They are calling out my name, Phoe-be, Phoe-be," exclaimed the surprised little girl. "They must live here."

"Notice the olive gray head, their black bills and whitish breast," the farmer explained as he came nearer. "Their white wing bars are so faint you can hardly see them."

"Can I stand on a ladder to see their nest?" she asked.

Uncle Phillip brought a sturdy ladder from the utility shed and was followed by Phil who by now was curious at what the two saw.

"This nest is made of mud and moss mixed with grass and stuck right up there on the rafters," Phil described from the top ladder rung.

"The inside is lined with fuzz from cattail pods, fine feathers, and look, there is some thread and string."

"Let me see," clamored Phoebe as she perched on the top also. "They are only 6 or 7 inches long, and look at them wagging their tails!"

Upon closer inspection of the nest, they found four small round white eggs. The nest was so flat they wondered if they would roll out. Both parents were busy catching grasshoppers, crickets, horse flies, and other insects. They did take turns sitting on the eggs, however.

"Phoebe and Phil, come quickly," Uncle Phillip called to the children the next day. They bolted down the driveway towards the milk shed, running as fast as they could. Even Philemon, barking and jumping and Phineas the cat joined the race. They all ran so fast they frightened the chickens scratching for food in the gravel.

"What happened?" both children cried out together breathlessly.

"Look in Phoebe's nest," Uncle Phillip pointed upwards. "Tell me what you see."

They both sprung up the ladder and peered down into the nest where the four white eggs were yesterday. Instead, they discovered three balls of fuzzy gray white feathers huddled together.

"The eggs have hatched," Phoebe whispered, "but there are only three." She looked down and saw one egg was smashed on the ground below.

"Look, the mother is bringing them a small grass hopper," Phil said. She stuffed the food down the small open beaks that suddenly appeared out of the fuzz balls.

Phoebe watched each day as the little white fluffy balls changed into gray brown feathers. The three babies were constantly jockeying around in the tiny nest until it appeared there was not enough room for all of them. The parents soon became used to the little girl watching their activities.

♂

♀

JB-96

Every time the birds sang, they seemed to call her by name. The day finally came when Phoebe and Phil had to return home to the city. After packing their bags, they went down to the milk shed for one last look at their tiny bird friends.

Climbing up the ladder for the very last time, Phoebe gave a sharp cry of alarm. "They're gone!"

"They must have fallen out," Phil said knowingly. "See, there is one on the ground below the nest."

As he stepped forward to replace it in the nest, the frightened bird fluttered its wings and took a solo flight across the yard to the apple tree. Landing on a small branch, it clung tenaciously as the nervous parent birds flitted about. Both long tails were bobbing up and down and they were repeating Phoebe's name again and again.

"Where are the others?" Phoebe inquired anxiously.

"There is one over in the maple tree," Uncle Phillip said as he joined the excited children.

"Look, they are all flying off into the woods."

Phoebe stared at the birds fluttering among the branches and waved a gentle goodby. Phil took down the ladder and vowed to look in the nest again next summer.

When Phoebe returned to school, she told everyone about her bird friends that called her by name. Never again did she regret having a name that no one else had. She now knew some Phoebes herself.

ALWISE EVENING RECORD

It was around five a.m. when I pushed the key into the front door lock of the *Alwise Evening Record.* The streets of the small Midwestern town were deserted except for a sweeper truck, which was cleaning up yesterday's Main Street debris. Several hard November frosts had stripped the trees of their foliage and their dark slender branches poked up into the moonlit sky like black tendrils. A street light threw gleaming yellow rays upon the gold letters of the newspaper office, painted there many years before by the founder and original owner, P. Saul Spedient. The inside of the building glowed with an eerie bluish night light shining from behind the office counter, where during the day, customers placed orders for printing or left classified ads.

The bolt fell away with a loud click and I swung the door open. Closing and locking it behind me, I headed directly through the main office to the printing shop out back. My first job as janitor was to light the gas burners on the linotype machines. Thus, the lead would be melted and ready to make type when the operators came in at seven. There were four machines and George Hanks on the first machine was supposed to be the fastest operator in Southern Michigan. There were always scraps of melted lead, spilled droplets of the glistening metal scattered around on the floor. I cleaned up these droppings and put them back into the master hopper where left over or used type was remelted. After lighting the machines and cleaning up the scrap lead, I wandered back towards the big flatbed press that printed the paper each afternoon.

148

Gathering up the torn newsprint, discarded ruined papers and other paper trash, I took it to a back room and threw the stuff into the paper baler. The back door led off this room to the alley and I noticed that someone had forgotten to put the bar back in place. A person could only open the door from the inside with the bar down. I shrugged my shoulders, slipped the bar back into place and filled the baler with paper. I couldn't see too well in the dim light, some of the papers in the baler felt damp. I stuffed the trash into the machine anyway. After applying screw pressure, I slipped the wires around the compressed mass, fastened them securely and took out the bale and set it aside. A truck came about every two weeks to pick up the two or three accumulated bales.

The task of cleaning up the layout tables was not too difficult as the editor, Don Mason, usually left unwanted lead type in a special area where I could easily gather it and throw it into the master melting pot. About once or twice a week, I had to add a new lead ingot to replenish lost metal. Using oiled red sawdust, I then swept the entire shop area and put the sweepings into the trash barrel. After polishing the presses, putting the stools, chairs and other items in order, I headed for the offices.

It was nearly six when I started cleaning up the rest room. Wilma Croft, secretary for both Jack Spedient, the publisher/owner and the editor, Don Mason, had recently been on my case about not cleaning it properly. So armed with cleanser, rags, brushes and air freshener, I was resolved to clean it thoroughly. I noticed some blood on my right hand, but couldn't find a cut or scratch. There was some on the washbowl also, perhaps one of the shop men had cut his hand on a machine. With vigor and purpose, I scrubbed it clean. The toilet was disinfected, flushed several times, and I even polished the mirror. Wilma couldn't complain about the rest room being dirty when she came in that day.

149

As I cleaned off the counter, I thought of how Mr. Spedient's son had helped me get the job. The son's real name was J. Saul Spedient, everyone called him "Speed" because of how fast he ran down the sidelines during College football games. Alwise was a town with a small college established by Rev. John Alwise on the banks of the Kalamazoo River in the 1830's. It had an excellent academic reputation and I had decided to attend the college for my pre-law education. Thanks to an Elks National Merit Award and a football scholarship, I was able to enroll.

Though Speed was a senior, he helped coach our freshman team so I got to know him pretty well. He had urged me to rush for the Tau Kappa Epsilon fraternity too, but I couldn't afford it. His father needed a custodian at the newspaper, so after meeting Mr. Spedient, I landed the job.

The Associated Press automatic teletype machine was clattering away when I went into Don Mason's office. I flipped on the light, gasped at the clutter and disorder on his desk, then emptied the waste basket into my trash bag. I dusted a little on the window sill looking out upon Main Street where dawn was turning the sky gray. I flipped off the switch and went into Mr. Spedient's office.

When I turned on the light, I was startled to see the owner/publisher sitting in his chair, slumped over his desk. His face was buried in the desk blotter and his arms hung limply at his sides. There was a pool of blood on the desk which was dripping slowly to the floor. A nauseating feeling hit my stomach; I felt dizzy and nearly passed out. I slid into a chair and stared at the scene in front of me.

"Mr. Spedient, Mr Spedient. Can you hear me?" I cried.

His pure white hair was matted with dark blood, his coat hung on the coat tree in the corner and his white shirt was splattered with blood. A few papers were scattered on the desk and a pen lay beside his right hand.

He did not answer. I gulped, rose slowly from my chair and went to the phone at the front desk. Searching through the white pages, I found the number of the police station and dialed.

"Hello, is this the police station?" I croaked into the mouthpiece.

"Yes, sir, Sullivan here. What can I do for you?"

"This is Tom Lear, the janitor over at the Evening Record. Something terrible has happened to Mr. Spedient and I think you should come right over." I spoke with a voice that seemed to come from another body. "Please hurry. I'll unlock the front door."

"Be right over, son." Mike Sullivan was the night duty policeman who occasionally stopped in at the paper on his nightly rounds. He often chatted with me and had become accustomed to seeing the lights on in the early morning and he knew I was just cleaning up the place.

I laid the receiver back on the hook and walked back into Mr. Spedient's office. The nausea had left me and my head was clear. It appeared to me that he had been struck on the back of his head with a heavy object. Who would do such a thing? He was well liked by his employees, served on the Board of Governors up at the College, was active in his church and community. There had been some racial disturbances at the foundry across the tracks about two or three months ago and he had taken a strong stand in favor of labor in his newspaper. He even got along well with the editor, George Mason, though office rumors indicated that George and Wilma were having an affair.

The clattering of the A-P machine, the smell of fresh blood and the crumpled body of my boss before me all seemed unreal. The dictaphone stood silent in a corner, his waste basket was still unemptied, his neat desk was soiled by pools of blood. Who would run the paper? Who would be my boss? Would I lose my job? I turned and went out front.

151

All the lights in the front office were blazing when Mike lumbered through the front door. He gave me a nod and I pointed to Mr. Spedient's office. The two of us walked by Wilma's desk, neatly clean with a picture of her teenage daughter staring back at us. The policeman glanced at Don Mason's cluttered office with the incessant pounding of the wireless machine carrying in the day's news from around the world. He then stopped at Mr. Spedient's office door and stared straight ahead.

"Well, Tom, you're right. This is beyond my experience. I'm going to call a homicide detective from Jackson. You haven't touched anything have you?"

"No, sir. I found him just like that while cleaning up the offices."

"When do the other employees get here?"

"It's usually about seven when the linotype operators show up. I leave for school after they get here."

" Well, you better plan to stay here until that detective gets here," Mike shook his head and went back out to the counter phone.

"Are you going to call his family?" I asked Mike as he dialed.

"I'll go out and tell them in person after Fred gets here."

Mike then went to the front door, put a police barricade across the front of the building and hung a "Closed" sign on the door.

"Can anyone get in the back door?" he asked me.

"Not as long as it is barred from the inside," I replied.

"Well, I'll stay and steer the employees home, " he said. "There won't be any paper today."

"Don Mason won't like that. He always puts out the paper, Sundays, holidays, always."

"We may spend the day asking questions of all the employees," Mike grimaced and made another phone call.

It was around nine when Fred Strang, the Jackson detective, showed up with two plain clothes members of the homicide squad. Fred sent Mike out to talk to the family and to arrange a meeting with them for that afternoon.

"Tom," Fred said, "I want you to stick around to answer a few questions after I complete my investigation."

Mr. Strang was an ordinary looking man, slightly overweight, in his mid-forties, I guessed. His balding head was covered with a small jaunty hat, and he even wore a plain looking tie hanging across his rumpled shirt. He wore a pair of horn rimmed glasses, thick as coke bottle bottoms, but through them, his keen blue eyes seemed to take in all the details of an investigation.

He carefully looked over the main office, the rest room, and surveyed the shop out back. When he came back, he went into Mr. Spedient's office and looked at the corpse sitting at his desk. I watched as his assistants took fingerprints from the light switch, which had a little blood on it. He took prints of the pen, a small statuette from behind the desk, the arms of the chair opposite the desk, and the door knob. He then took careful measurements of where the body was in relation to the door, the desk and chair. It reminded me of a Perry Mason movie I had seen.

The three men then carefully stretched out the body on the floor. The sight of Mr. Spedient's face about did me in, so I went out and sat in a chair at the counter. Don Mason started knocking on the door and signaled for me to let him in. I suspected he had forgotten his key. I gestured toward Mr. Spedient's office and shrugged my shoulders.

"Mr. Strang," I called, "Don Mason, the editor wants to get in. Shall I let him?"

"I'll speak to him," he replied. He came out of the office and went to the front door.

He slid open the glass door and let Mr. Mason in. I could barely hear their conversation, but Don turned and went back out. Mr. Strang returned to Mr. Spedient's office.

So it was with each of the office girls, the ad manager and the shop help. He spoke briefly with each of them and they left again without entering the office or shop. When the coroner came, however, Fred ushered him into the dead man's office. I could see the doctor doing some preliminary examinations of the body.

By this time, I could see out the front window that a crowd was beginning to gather around the front of the newspaper building. The police barricade, the employees leaving and the "closed" sign on the door had perked everyone's curiosity. When the coroner's ambulance arrived to take away the covered guerney, no one needed a newspaper to tell them what had happened. Several of my college friends were in the crowd and waved at me sitting behind the counter.

When the body left, people began drifting away, and soon there were only a few left. Mr. Strang came out of the murder room and invited me into Don Mason's office.

"Please sit down," he motioned me to a chair beside the cluttered desk and he plumped himself down in Don's swivel chair. "Tell me what you know of this affair."

"Well, I came to work as usual this morning at five. I turned on the linotypes." The thought suddenly came to me that I should turn them off before I left if there was not going to be a paper that day. "Then I cleaned up the shop, baled the scrap paper, cleaned the rest room, main office and was about to clean up Mr. Spedient's when I found him." I shuddered again at the grisly sight that had greeted me when I had flicked on the light switch.

"Was there anything unusual that you noticed?" He peered at me through his thick lens, and took out a small notebook.

"Not really," I replied.

He was looking at my hands, then at my broad shoulders. "What position do you play in football?"

"Linebacker on the freshman team."

"Do you know the Spedient family?" He was probing a little deeper.

"Speed Spedient, that's Mr. Spedient's son, plays varsity football and got me the job here. He has a daughter, also a freshman, but I don't know her very well. His wife teaches debate at the local high school and I met her in high school when our team defeated theirs in the debate tournament finals."

"How about you and your family?" Mr. Strang was jotting a few notes on his pad.

"My father is just a milkman, my mother a housewife. I am the oldest of five kids and the first one to attend college, pre-law. Thanks to a couple of scholarships, I was able to come to Alwise."

"Well, Tom," he said in a kindly way, "I want you to come on down to the station where we can fingerprint you. You can call your folks from there and then I'll let you get back to class."

"Shall I come back to work tomorrow morning?" It seemed as though my job was evaporating.

"I'll let you know, or Mr. Mason will contact you when the paper will resume publication. Right now, we have an investigation to complete. I must talk with the family and there may be a hearing in a few days after we get the coroner's report. If you think of anything that might be pertinent to the case, call me at the police station."

155

Of course, the campus was abuzz with talk of the murder at the town's newspaper. Other kids looked at me with a peculiar glance, some of my friends avoided me as if I were guilty of the crime. I began feeling isolated and alone, especially when my football team mates would stop conversations as I approached. No one saw Speed or his sister around the quad or in classes.

The only other news that week was when a big fight broke out between the TKE and Sigma Chi fraternities when the TKE's accused the Sigma Chi's of stealing their statue mascot from their frat house. Denials, insults, and accusations almost made the murder case seem like a minor crime in comparison.

After a couple of days, Don Mason called and said they were resuming publication of the paper so they would need me to work. I hesitated about returning to the office, but Mike Sullivan met me there the first morning. It was while baling up the scrap paper, I remembered about the dampness I felt the morning of the crime. I told Mike about it, he jotted down a note.

It was difficult to concentrate on my studies as a thousand thoughts ran through my mind. My folks were a comfort, but indicated they could not afford a lawyer to help me. They thought I probably wouldn't need one as I was not charged with anything. Mr. Strang called and said a hearing would be held at one o'clock Friday afternoon in the police station. I assured him I would be there.

The hearing room was crowded with people. I saw Speed and his sister sitting with their mother at one end of the long walnut table. A man in a business suit with tie and briefcase was at their side, probably their lawyer. Don Mason, Wilma Croft and George Hanks were seated next to me at the side of the table. A court stenographer sat at the corner, poised, ready to record the day's events. A large captain's chair at the other end of the table sat dignified and empty.

Side chairs away from the table held Mr. Strang, Mike Sullivan and the plain clothed policemen. On the other side of the table, I saw the coroner and a couple of strangers whom I did not recognize.

The afternoon sun streaked through the venetian blinds, throwing shadow bars across the scene. The Chief of Police with braid on his cap and shoulder bars, then entered and sat in the captain's chair.

"We are here today to have an inquiry into the death of Mr. Jack Spedient, owner/publisher of the Alwise Evening Record." The Chief hesitated a moment and looked at Mrs. Spedient wiping away a tear. "First, we will have a report from the coroner."

The lanky doctor shuffled a few papers in front of him, pushed a stray strand of gray hair away from his eyes, and started his report. "I found the deceased at his desk. He had been dead about six hours from a severe blow to the back of his head. The autopsy showed a cerebral concussion, hemorrhage and subdural hematoma, any of which could explain his demise."

Six hours, I thought, that was long before I had even come to work.

"Do you have any idea what the instrument of death was?" The Chief asked quietly.

The coroner looked askance at Mr. Strang and replied, "A large blunt object with a few sharp corners. Perhaps Mr. Strang can answer that question."

The Chief looked at the detective and said, "We will have your report a little later. You can answer that question then."

"We need to hear from Tom Lear, the janitor who found the deceased." The Chief looked at me and continued, "Do you want a lawyer to help you?"

"No, sir," I replied. "I can't afford one."

"We can get the court to appoint one for you, if you wish," he said.

"I'll just tell it the way I remember," I said. Speed looked at me in a funny way. Did he think I was the guilty one? He acted like some of the kids up at school who seemed to blame me for what had happened. I wished my folks had come to give me moral support.

I related the events of that morning the best I could remember. Don Mason, Wilma Croft and George Hanks then gave brief reports about their long time employment by the Evening Record. They said they were denied entrance into the office by the police on the morning of the murder. After their brief testimony, they were excused.

"Mr. Strang," the Chief turned to the detective, "you may give your report and your findings now."

"Thank you, sir. I believe we can resolve this matter if you will allow me to ask a few questions of certain persons who are present."

"You may proceed," the Chief said. "This is not a trial, just an inquest to uncover facts. Anyone may refuse to answer, that's okay."

"First, I would like to ask Tom Lear a few more questions."

My heart skipped a beat, I thought I had told him everything I knew about the case.

"Tom," he said facing me directly across the table, "do you know there was blood on the light switch of Mr. Spedient's office *along with your fingerprints?*"

I blushed, "I didn't see the blood, but I turned on the light when I found him there."

"Were you sitting in the chair across from Mr. Spedient in his office? *We found your fingerprints on the arms of that chair.*" Mr. Strang's question gave me a sinking feeling in my stomach. Glancing at the Spedient family, I saw Speed drop his eyes to his hands, his mother shook her head while his sister took a deep breath.

Pausing for a moment to recall the scene, I replied, "Yes, sir. After finding Mr. Spedient in his office, I nearly fainted and had to sit in that chair to recover from the shock."

The detective's eyes appeared huge as he stared through his myopic lenses. Mr. Strang then looked over at the Spedient family and resumed his questions. His blue green tie looked out of place on his rumpled shirt and his worn business suit was creased as if he had slept in it.

"Also, Mr. Lear, do you know that a heavy metal sculpture with Mr. Spedient's blood on the base, was found in a bale of paper *that you baled up and set out in the alley.?*"

I stopped and pondered his question. So that accounted for the dampness I had felt in the waste paper that morning.

"No, sir, I didn't know that. It didn't seem any heavier than usual."

"Can you explain why you scrubbed blood off the washbowl that morning *when usually you are negligent in cleaning the rest room?*"

So Wilma had told them about my dirty rest rooms. Was he going to charge me for the murder? Maybe I should have asked for a lawyer. "Wilma had gotten after me for having a dirty washbowl, so I cleaned it special to satisfy her."

"Was there anyone else at the newspaper office the morning you found the deceased?" Mr. Strang gave me his inquisitive look.

"No, sir," I replied. "Not that I was aware of."

"Did you find the back door unbarred when you arrived that morning?"

"Yes, sir. Just like I told you before. Anyone could have come in the back."

Mr. Strang then rustled through his papers, turned over several of them to scan the back of the pages. Speed had a wry grimace upon his face as he sat tapping his fingers on the table. He would not establish eye contact with me, so certainly he must think I did it.

"What time did you arrive at the Evening Record office on the day you found Mr. Spedient?" Fred scribbled something on a sheet of paper before him.

"My usual time, five o'clock in the morning, " I answered.

"Now, Chief," Mr. Strang addressed the portly police captain, "may I ask a few questions of J. Saul Spedient?"

"Of course," the Chief replied. "Now Mr. Spedient, this is just a hearing to get at the facts of your father's death, so do not hesitate to answer Mr. Strang's questions."

His lawyer spoke up at that point. "It appears to me you have enough evidence to arrest that young man for murder." He pointed at me and continued. "My client should not have to answer any questions."

Speed's face was pale and he appeared nervous. His father's death must have hit him pretty hard. He had been due to go into the newspaper business after graduation and eventually run the Evening Record.

"Chief, I think it's important that we ask young Spedient a few questions to establish all the facts in this case," Fred leaned forward and tapped his pen on his papers.

"Please answer Mr. Stang's questions, if you please," the Chief instructed the son.

After the preliminary questions of identification, relationship to the deceased, and his role in the family, Mr. Strang continued his questions.

"Mr. Spedient," Fred Strang's kindly voice resonated through the room, "can you tell me where you were the evening of November 24, the night before your father died?"

"Well, sir," Speed's voice was soft and barely audible, "I was playing cards at the Tau Kappa Epsilon house."

"What time did you leave the fraternity house?" Mr. Strang asked him.

"It must have been about eleven o'clock."

"What time did you get home?" The probing question seemed to rattle the senior halfback like a tackle from behind.

"I don't know, perhaps eleven thirty," he replied.

"Mrs. Spedient," Fred Strang addressed the mother, "can you tell us what time your son arrived home on the night in question?"

She wiped a tear from her eye, looked at her son and answered. "Yes, it was one o'clock in the morning. I saw the clock on the bedroom night stand and wondered why Jack wasn't home yet."

"Did you stop at the newspaper office on your way home?" The directness of the question startled Speed. His lawyer appeared as if he wanted to say something, but remained silent.

"Er, no, I didn't." The unflappable popular college senior appeared flustered.

With that reply, Mr. Strang reached under the table and pulled up a bronzed sculpture with a heavy marble base. The nude female figure stood about a foot high and was posed in a provocative manner. Dark stains were still evident on the white marble base.

"Have you ever seen this statue before?" Mr. Strang looked directly at Speed's ashen face through his thick glass lenses.

"No, sir."

"I object to this line of questions," Speed's lawyer almost jumped up.

161

"Chief, this man is lying." Mr. Strang looked pitifully at Mrs. Spedient. "This sculpture has been on display at the TKE House for many years. All fraternity members have been well acquainted with it and she even has a name, Ginger Cookie. She turned up missing the night of Mr. Spedient's murder. The TKE's thought it was stolen by the Sigma Chi's but we found it wrapped in a bale of scrap paper. It was soiled with Mr. Jack Spedient's blood and we also found *the fingerprints of J. Saul Spedient on it.* This man is under arrest for the murder of his father."

Speed collapsed in his chair. His mother clutched her chest.

"I object to this accusation," his lawyer piped up. "That boy is the guilty one," he said pointing at me.

"The hearing is over," the Chief rose and marched out of the room. "We will turn the case over to the Prosecuting Attorney."

We anticipated that everything would be repeated at Speed's trial. As it turned out, he broke down and confessed to the crime after all the incriminating evidence was presented to him. Mr. Strang had first suspected me as the guilty one. The six hour time difference between time of death and finding the body, made him suspect some one else. Especially when he got the testimony of the street sweeper who collaborated the five o'clock time I had arrived at the newspaper. Besides, he couldn't figure any motive for me to kill Mr. Spedient.

It came out later that Speed had had a big row with his father over who was going to run the paper after his graduation. He had taken the TKE statue down to the paper for the local news photographer to get a good picture of it. Speed knew his father was working late and would let him in to drop off the statue.

162

While there, father and son had gotten into another big discussion about the future. In a fit of anger, Speed had struck his father on the back of the head with Ginger Cookie. Looking for a place to hide the murder weapon, he had buried it in the scrap paper of the baler. He had washed off his hands in the rest room, unbarred the back door and left, arriving home about one o'clock. He had figured that I would be blamed for his father's death when I came to work in the morning.

After talking with several employees and the Spedient family, Mr. Strang had found out about the big fight between the son and father. So when I had mentioned to Mike that felt damp papers in the baler, they had retrieved Cookie Ginger from the paper bale, fingerprints and blood tests proved that the young Spedient was guilty.

Mr. Mason ran the paper and I had my job back until I graduataed and went to the University Law School. I sent an announcement to both Mike Sullivan and Fred Strang.

ONE WAY OUT

A loud noise startled Jack Craven from his sound sleep. He sat up in the darkness of his Michigan cabin deep in the north woods and glanced out the window. He tried to see if lightening would explain the rumbling from across the lake. There were no flashes and the sound did not fade away like distant thunder. Jeri, his wife of forty five years, was still asleep with her good ear buried in the pillow. She was usually the one who heard woodchucks under the cabin floor or the snap of a mouse trap capturing another victim.

Jack tumbled out of bed, which was an heirloom from his parents. His father had brought it to the cabin after his grandparents had died in the forties. Its walnut head and foot board matched the two dark grained dressers. He pulled on his leather slippers and went out onto the screened in front porch to investigate. The southwestern sky was glowing yellow red and a continuous thundering noise filtered through the pines. He shook his head, went back into the bedroom and pulled on his denim jeans and slipped on his heavy rubber boots. After slipping on his light weight flannel jacket, he grabbed the keys to the 4X4 on his way out.

The dim dial of the clock read 2:15 as he closed the door softly behind him. The summer night was cool, but its usual dampness was missing. It had been several weeks since it had rained. There was no breeze and the dark trees stood like a jagged solid black wall surrounding the cabin.

Jack paused, took off his glasses and rubbed his sleepy eyes. He plopped his hunting cap over his thinning white hair and climbed into his vehicle. It started right up with a quiet purr. He backed into the turn around drive, and eased the jeep into the driveway. The main road was about half mile away. To get to the other side of the lake, he would have to drive over a bridge crossing the creek.

His lean frame bounced and jarred as he hit the tree roots protruding randomly in the two lane dirt tracks. He noticed a raccoon scooting up a tamarack tree near a large upturned fir stump. He began speculating about the cause of the roaring noise as he broke into the clearing running along side the highway.

Jack braked, jumped down from the driver's seat and unhooked the galvanized metal gate. He noticed the lock was open and dangling from its rusty metal chain. Jeri must have forgotten to fasten it, or maybe he had failed to lock it himself. When a man got to be sixty five, he tended to forget things. He swung the gate open and latched it to a cedar post planted there beside the drive.

County Road 38 was deserted. He pulled the 4X4 onto the asphalt pavement and headed west. The roaring noise and sky glow increased in intensity as he approached the road leading back to gas well number 4, nicknamed "Ed Moses." He smiled as he thought of the four wells on their property which the gas company had given names of famous athletes. He had resisted drilling wells for several years, but with neighbors all around striking gas at 1600 feet, he finally gave in. With his own retirement not far off and the added promised income, he had finally yielded to the pressure of the Saturn Exploration Co. They had convinced him of the advisability of drilling for gas in a deep shale layer known as the Antrim shale.

It was two years ago that he had watched with interest the clearing of the well sites and the drilling rigs at work. The price of gas was high, the tax write-offs were favorable, a steady income was assured, so things seemed to have worked out. At that moment, however, he wondered if something had gone wrong with the gas well.

Jack parked his vehicle at the entrance of the road leading to the well site and clambered out. He began walking slowly through the trees toward the increasingly loud sound. He also remembered that gas right from the ground did not smell so a leak might be hard to detect. Even a spark or heat from the car could cause an explosion.

After his eyes adapted to the darkness, the white sand tracks of the road gleamed in the night. The sky glowed red over the forest and seemed brighter about where the gas road ended. The roar was now distinctly coming from that location. About a hundred yards from where the road opened into the clearing around the gas well, he finally could see what had happened. The little green well house had been blown off its cement base and a stream of fire was shooting straight up to the stars.

It was now apparent why Saturn had insisted on clearing an acre of ground around each well. The gas pouring from the well pipe was burning like a Bunsen burner, harmlessly into the atmosphere. It looked like one of the burn off pipes he had seen at the Mt. Pleasant oil refinery.

Jack ran back to his jeep, and searched for his CB radio. He remembered it was on the workbench in the shed where he had placed it after removing it the night before. He jumped into the driver's seat and sped back to the cabin. Dashing into the back door, he found Jeri in her robe with an alarmed look on her face.

"What's the matter, Jack?"

"Ed Moses blew up and the well's burning," Jack replied, reaching for the phone. He quickly dialed an emergency number and waited impatiently for the buzzer to be answered.

"Darden?" Jack spoke urgently when a sleepy voice responded to the ring. "Ed Moses has blown up and the gas well's on fire!"

"Anybody hurt? " Darden said.

"No, it's just shooting flames into the sky."

"Thanks, Jack, I'll have someone over there right away."

Jack slammed down the receiver and turned to Jeri. "Never should have let those fellows put in those wells. They might start a forest fire or something!"

"Do we have to get out of here?" Jeri asked.

"No, I don't think there is any immediate danger. I'm going back over there to watch things until that well crew gets here."

Later that morning, Jack came in and removed his boots. Jeri was sipping her coffee at the breakfast table. Slipping into his moccasins, he stopped at the bathroom to remove the soot, dirt and grime from his wrinkled face. He moved slower than usual in his morning clean up chores. When finished, he finally pulled up a log chair with its red vinyl seat covering. His father had built the set of six chairs shortly after coming to the cabin. They matched the sturdy round breakfast table. After some fruit, a couple pieces of toast and his glass of milk, he turned his tired blue eyes toward Jeri and spoke.

"The Saturn fellows told me someone deliberately blew up the well house."

"Why, Jack," Jeri responded, "who would do that? Besides, how can they tell?" She always had questions.

"The well house was caved in from the outside," Jack said. "If the explosion had occurred from the inside, the walls would have been blown out. They finally did get the thing stopped by pinching off the pipe below the ground surface."

"Do you have any idea who would have done it?"

"Not really," Jack paused in deep thought before he continued.

"I did have an argument with that new neighbor down the road several days ago. You know, that Paul what's-his-name who moved onto those twenty acres with his wife and six kids. That house he's got is pretty flimsy. I don't see how he can get a brood like that into it."

"What were you fighting about?" Jeri asked.

"Wasn't really a fight, I just asked him to keep his kids off our property, and his dogs too. With the drought this summer, the woods being tinder dry, all we need is to have a bunch of reckless kids set the woods on fire!"

"Is that black lab that came around here the other day, their dog?" Jeri asked. "He ran down and jumped into the lake and scared away the loon that was out there fishing."

"Yes, that's one of their four dogs. The driveway is not even safe to walk in anymore, with all the dog crap out there by the gate."

"His wife seems pleasant enough. She works at the post-office as a substitute rural carrier." Jeri poured him another glass of milk and gave him another slice of toast.

"Don Mason says he works at Wal-Mart every night. His father is the new Lutheran minister in town. The rumors are that this Paul fellow has served some time in jail."

"Well, he is taking care of his family, let's give him credit for that." Jeri looked askance at her husband. "Why do you think he did it?"

168

"I really didn't say he did, but who else would have done it?"

"Is there anyway you can prove that Paul blew up the well?"

"Not really," Jack said, "but Saturn is going to investigate."

"Well, dear," Jeri gave her husband a queer look, "if there ever was a forest fire across the driveway, how would we ever get out of here? I've been telling you for years that we need another route of exit."

"I know, I know." Jack again looked worried. "I'm going to call that guy about bull-dozing another driveway up through the north woods. I've been meaning to do it for some time." He thought about their home deep in the middle of the pine woods. "You're right, Jeri, we need another exit route."

He continued talking quietly, "Putting in the new fence and gate out front, completion of the new screened porch and several other projects have kept me from taking any action on that second road. It's about a mile through those dense pines to the fire road that runs off to Buhl Lake."

Jeri replied, "That is the exact opposite direction of our present driveway access road."

Later that morning, Jack called Larry's Heavy Equipment Shop about bulldozing a road. The pleasant voiced woman who answered the phone said that Larry had broken his ankle and was in a cast. It would be about 3-4 weeks before he could come out and do it. Jack shrugged his shoulders and asked her to have Larry call him when available.

Jack spent the next two days fixing the dock, cleaning out the boat house and building a table for the new screened in porch. He bought some fluorescent tape to mark a trail through the north woods so Larry would know exactly where to bullldoze the new road. It wound around the swamp made by beavers damming up the spring fed creek feeding the main lake.

Jack planned to have the new road run along an old railroad bed. This had been used in the 1890's when virgin white pines had been logged off to build Chicago and Detroit. Several of the huge old stumps were still rotting away, so gigantic that even a hundred years later, they had not completely decayed.

He also picked up a bunch of used baby pampers, old beer cans, and other trash that had been dumped in front of his main gate. When Jack went over to Paul's to ask him about it, the neighbor denied any knowledge of why the trash was there. Soon after, he noticed that the chain holding the padlock had been cut with a bolt cutter. Several strands of new barbed wire fence were also broken or cut. The discussion about the garbage had gotten nowhere, so he decided not to confront his neighbor with these minor problems. Jack did mention it to Darden from Saturn who was investigating the gas well explosion.

Ed Moses was back in production after about three days with a new tin well house and a freshly painted green donkey engine pushing the cam wheel steadily up and down. The graph on the wall of the green shed showed production gradually increasing and a new "No Trespassing" sign was displayed prominently on the door. The old damaged well house, pipes and destroyed motor had been hauled off for further investigation by the gas company.

When the urgent chores were finished, Jack went blackberry picking, canoeing and fishing with Jeri. It was almost as if the couple were spending their honeymoon again on the lake, tramping through the woods, and sleeping soundly at night.

The summer seemed to be drifting back into a lazy mode and the couple soon forgot about the gas well explosion. Jack put the sprinkler on the brown lawn grass and noted the leaves and sticks on the forest trails were cracking loudly with each step as the days continued without rain. The beaver pond at the outlet of the lake was low, and the swamp mud became caked and cracked.

Jack tried to ignore his neighbor and patiently cleaned up the pop cans and beer bottles strewn along the front of his property. He patiently cleaned up the dog dirt, repaired the broken gate chain and lock. The small neighbor kids usually ran for home when they saw him coming though he tried to be friendly with them. He thought of his own grandchildren who liked to come to "Craven's Haven" for fishing, hiking, and play.

One evening, a couple weeks later, Jack and Jeri had just finished their supper on the porch, eating on the new octagonal table that Jack had constructed. The sun was getting low over the lake when a doe and her fawn sauntered across the foot path down by the dock. Stopping to take a drink from the shore, their ears swiveled like radar screens before they bounded into the marsh with their white tails flying. A porcupine waddled across the dry lawn and headed for the trail to the skunk shed just inside the firs and spruces of the north woods. The cry of a loon could be heard echoing across the lake.

Yellow shafted flickers were taking a dust bath in the sand path and digging for ants. A gentle breeze shook the silvery leaves of the quaking aspen poplars and white birch trunks turned a cadmium yellow with the late sun. Dragon flies glided like helicopters across the evening air and frogs could be heard croaking from the marsh. Cedar wax wings darted after insects, catching them in mid-air before returning to dead tree limbs.

Jeri sniffed the air for a moment before speaking. "Were you burning trash in the barrel out back?"

Jack looked fondly over at Jeri sitting relaxed in her chair.

"No, not tonight, honey. Did you burn something making dinner?"

"If I gave you burnt offerings, you'd know it."

Jack laughed at a joke which dated from Jeri's early days of cooking.

"Well, I smell smoke. Do you?" Jeri was the one with the keen sense of smell in the family.

"As a matter of fact, I do," he said.

Jeri looked out over the front yard to the lake, "The sun is looking kind of red too, for being so high in the sky."

Jack got up and pulled his boots on and hitched up his pants. "Maybe it's finally going to rain." He looked at the sky carefully and said, "Think I'll mosey on down the driveway to see if I can find any reason for the smoke smell. Want to walk along?"

"No thanks, dear," Jeri replied. "I had my walk earlier this afternoon. I'll stay here and clean up the supper dishes."

Jack sprayed on some "Off" mosquito dope, though the mosquitoes had not been bad this summer without any rain. He pulled on his hat with a wild turkey feather stuck in the hat band and headed down the main driveway. He enjoyed these evening walks in the quiet of the forest where he frequently saw grouse, squirrels and other wildlife. He still was concerned about the strong smell of burning wood. Perhaps his neighbor was having a barbecue or finally burning his trash instead of dumping it on his property.

He had gone as far as the sand pit when he saw a coyote running across its rim. The animal was so shy, Jack seldom saw this creature, though he had seen its tracks countless times. The sky was turning dark and he thought maybe it really would rain. He heard a strange crackling sound ahead, near where the road went between six huge pines. He picked up his pace and hurried towards the front gate.

As Jack came around the bend where the deer blind was hidden just off the road, he stopped and stared at the driveway in front of him.

About three hundred yards away, trees on both sides of the road were burning like Olympic torches. The flames were leaping from treetop to treetop. The underbrush was also ablaze and the driveway itself presented a solid wall of fire. He felt a strong breeze and could see the inferno moving toward him rapidly. Running down the driveway at full speed was Paul's black lab.

He cried out loud, "My God, a forest fire!"

He turned and ran back down the road toward their house. The dog passed him as he streaked by the sand pit. Bursting into the living room, he yelled at Jeri, "Forest fire down the driveway and heading towards the cabin!"

He reached for the phone and rapidly dialed "911".

"Forest fire at 8300 Mancelona Road! That's in Wilderness Valley!" He slammed the receiver back on the hook and looked wildly at Jeri. Just then the lights went out and Jack realized the power lines running from the road had succumbed to the flames. Without electricity, the water pump was useless.

"What?" Jeri wiped her hands on her apron. She grabbed the fly swatter and swung it at a fly on the sink. "What shall we do?"

"We can't drive out, too much fire on the driveway!"

He glanced around quickly. He went out on the front porch and saw smoke billowing over the south woods. The black lab was running down the path to the lake.

"We still have one way out. Quick, down to the lake!"
Jack grabbed Jeri and pushed her out the front door. They
bolted down the path to the boathouse. The dog ran out on
the dock and plunged into the water.

They just got the aluminum boat into the water when the
fire storm broke into the cabin clearing. Using the oars
with all his aging strength, Jack pulled the boat away from
the dock. Jack could feel the heat from exploding pines
radiating down the path. Even the blue spruce trees he had
planted several years ago on either side of the front yard
went off like roman candles.

Pulling rapidly and powerfully, Jack moved the boat out
into the middle of the lake. Jeri sat stunned in the stern,
looking at her home being engulfed with flames. Their
collection of antique furniture, pictures of family and
friends, Jack's books, everything was being consumed by
this red devil. The pines, maples, oaks, poplars, firs and
spruces exploded like firecrackers. Soon even the boat
house was on fire.

They watched as the jeep burst into a ball of fire. The
electric power wires leading to the cabin melted and power
poles fell over like burnt matches. The shed blew up when
the fire reached the gasoline Jack used for his power
mower, chain saw and generator. Windows popped out of the
cabin, the new front porch was reduced to a charred
skeleton quickly. In a few minutes, the fire storm raced
across the yard to the north wood lot.

Jeri began crying softly and Jack put his arm around
her shoulders gently. They watched their retirement hopes
and dreams melting before their stinging eyes. A beaver
swam around the lake, having abandoned its house on the
shore. It smacked its tail when close to their boat and
disappeared beneath the illuminated surface of the water.

The fire's reflection danced across the dark lake surface silhouetting the forms of the couple and their lonely boat. The sun had disappeared beneath the dark row of trees across the lake while the sky had an eerie red glow. A pair of ducks flew twice around before fading into the twilight.

A green water snake skimmed the water and two deer swam towards them, heading for the opposite shore. The labrador was swimming steadily across the lake. Dense black clouds filled the air and soot and smoke wafted over their heads. Jeri began coughing and choking so Jack took his handkerchief, dipped it in the water and put it over her nostrils. They both crouched low in the boat. Jack watched their over turned Kevlar canoe melt into a shapeless plastic mass. He began rowing steadily toward the opposite side of the lake. A few drops of rain began falling and mixed with the tears running down Jeri's face.

The next morning, it took several minutes for Jack to awake and remember where he was. He suddenly realized he was at Don Mason's, a good friend who had put them up for the night. His clearing mind remembered that after reaching the west shore, he and Jeri had hiked with the waiting black lab about two miles through the rain to the main road. There the fire fighters were congregated with their engines and rescue equipment. They had indicated the damage was so severe at the cabin, they feared the Cravens had perished in the conflagration. The soaking wet clothes clinging to their chilled and tired bodies were all that remained of their possessions.

Thanks to the rain and fire fighters, the blaze had consumed only about 500 acres and was contained shortly after midnight. Jack learned the fire had started at Paul's house which had burned to the ground also. The fire had spread there to the forest around Jack's cabin.

The fire chief had said a lot of trees were lost as well as the two houses. Fortunately, Paul had managed to get his family into their car and they had escaped down County Road 38. The entire bunch, with all the dogs except the black lab, were gone.

It was Don who drove Jack and Jeri over to see the charred remains of the cabin and forest. Jeri wanted to leave the area immediately but Jack persuaded her to think it over before making any quick judgment. They realized that insurance would cover the loss of the structures. The antiques, the photographs, and home movies could not be redeemed no matter where they went. While they stood viewing the devastation, the Fire Marshall drove up in his car with the black lab sitting in the back seat.

"Well, Jack," the Marshall said, "We have established that the fire at your neighbor's was deliberately set."

"What, an arsonist?" Jack stared at the man. "Who would do that?"

"Paul did it himself. Probably to collect the insurance, though he had been in prison for having set fires before."

"Where is he now?" Jack was curious about this sudden turn of events. "The police caught him with his family in Traverse City."

Jeri piped up, "What's happening to his family?"

"Well, his father has gone over there to make arrangements for them with social services. Paul, of course, is in the county jail."

"Did he blow up the gas well too?" Jack asked the Marshall. "Saturn thought so, but could not prove it."

"Yes, he has confessed to that also. Said he was jealous of your situation here on the lake, your gas well income, and all your trees."

Jack held Jeri's hand as they stared at the charred remains of their home, their sheds and their car. Bleak burned trees stood along the driveway, some which were still smoldering. All were deep black from the rain.

Looking into each others moist eyes, they realized their forest had come back after raging fires a hundred years before. The black lab jumped out of the car and sat looking at them. Jack placed his grizzled hand upon its friendly head. It was then they decided to rebuild and replant. It was the only way out.

178

TWELVE WORDS FROM A JAR

<u>Words</u>: dance, house, automobile, fence, sing,
play, drive, drink, black, large, soft, great.

Sing and dance, play on the fence
    and drive the automobile away.
Drink only in the black house
    where the large and great will sing.
Don't drink and drive! Sing,
    dance and watch them play.
We are talking of the large,
the soft, but not of the black.

<u>Words</u>: blows, read, dawn, sleep, meeting, card,
modern, swoon, producer, clicks, sheet, walk.

Send me a card and arrange a meeting,
    let me read it before dawn blows.
Pull the modern sheet over my head,
    while the producer clicks his boards.
Just then, I say, I swoon away,
    my profound sleep lasts until dawn.
The producer walks into the meeting,
    my modern card finally blows up.

<u>Words</u>: voice, paper, terrible, character, clicks,
select, modern, habits, bearing, lock, saint, water.

This terrible character has a raspy voice,
    he clicks his teeth and is overbearing.
Even the nuns in their black and white habits,
    lock their doors and pray to their blessed saint.
A real Frankenstein, will he select me
as his newest modern victim?
    They say he works both sides
    of the city water supply.